The Bridge Today 1,001 Workbook

— DUPLICATE AND TOURNAMENT EDITION —

by

Frank Stewart

To Rose Fensterheim

Best wishes!

Frank Stewart

Edited by Pamela and Matthew Granovetter
Cover by Tom Donnelly

Other books by Frank Stewart:

Better Bridge for the Advancing Player
Winning Defense for the Advancing Player
Frank Stewart's Contract Bridge Quiz Book
The Bridge Player's Comprehensive Guide to Defense
A Christmas Stocking
The Devyn Press Bridge Teacher's Manuals
and Student Texts. Volumes 1-4
The Bridge Books, Volumes 1-4

granovetter books
18 Village View Bluff
PO Box F
Ballston Lake, NY 12019
(518) 899-6670

Printed in the United States of America
ISBN 0-940257-07-6

BRIDGE TABLE OF CONTENTS

* When looking for the first page of a chapter,
look in the upper left-hand pages for an even # page,
upper right-hand pages for an odd # page.

Author's Acknowledgments

Various bridge periodicals — notably *The Bridge World, The Contract Bridge Bulletin* and the late lamented *Popular Bridge* — were the sources of a few of the deals in this book. Other deals came from the World Championship books published by the American Contract Bridge League.

Players are often referred to as "he" as a convenience.

Editors' Note

The bridge answers in this book are, for the most part, the popular and accepted practice of the top expert players in the world in the year 1990. However, partnership agreements (and time) often play a role in the meaning of a bid or play. Therefore, if you disagree with a few of the answers, you may be correct — in your style of play. The author has taken this into account in some of the answers, mentioning other ways of playing specific bids or sequences. There are no 100% answers in bridge; there are, however, probabilities and logic. We think you will find these quizzes not only fun to do, but stimulating and educational as well.

How To Use This Book

This book was designed to test, educate and stimulate the duplicate and tournament bridge player. The pages are meant to be written in, with plenty of space for notes. Do each chapter in one sitting, writing your answers next to the problems in the book. After you have completed all the problems in a chapter, go to the answers and check your results.

With the exception of the chapter title pages, there are no page numbers. However, you will find it easy to locate the answers to the quizzes:

346-352

[sample question page]

The quiz numbers on each page can be found at the top left or right-hand side of each page. Quiz numbers are boxed, as in the illustration on the left.

Answer pages, located immediately after each chapter's quizzes, have the word "ANSWERS" next to the quiz numbers. Answer numbers appear in the upper corner but are not boxed.

ANSWERS 493-496

[sample answer page]

Time to take out your pencil and get to work.

The Bridge Today 1,001 Workbook

For C.H.

How's Your Basic Bidding?

NOW HEAR THIS, bridge enthusiasts. The best part of anyone's game — *anyone's* — is a firm grasp of the fundamentals. Here's a simple exercise to make sure you don't suffer from any basic-type shortcomings in the bidding.

I. Opening Bids

What is your opening call as dealer, none vulnerable, on the following hands? The game is matchpoints.

Q853	K75	AQ106532	7	K
K64	Q109653	A87	KJ10653	Q74
Q64	AJ6	863	--	AQ53
AJ5	7	--	KQ10842	J7542
_P_	_2H_	_1S_	_1C_	_1C_
1	2	3	4	5

1064	AQJ95	106542	Q	65
Q4	A4	5	K54	54
AQ75	8	AQJ5	AJ95	AQ54
AQ64	Q10763	AQ6	K10763	AK1063
_1C_	_1S_	_1D_	_1C_	_1C_
6	7	8	9	10

4	AQ73	7	AJ75	--
KJ6	6	A864	AK64	AKQ8
AK97	K1065	AK64	Q964	AKJ83
AJ1053	AJ63	K1075	7	AQ75
_1D_	_1C_	_1C_	_1D_	_2C_
11	12	13	14	15

AK10973	J7	AQ	AQJ85	6
AK6	KQ1064	J1075	Q107653	974
AK4	AJ7	AQ753	K5	764
7	KQ7	K8	—	QJ9654

2♣ ___	1H ___	1NT ___	1♠ 1S ___	P ___
16	17	18	19	20

II. Responses

Your partner deals. Give the correct response to an opening one-bid in each of the four suits and 1NT (15-17 points).

	7	K75	964	9
	Q107532	A1075	AQ6	K953
	A53	K64	KJ53	A54
	J53	QJ2	AK4	KJ632

PARTNER	YOU	YOU	YOU	YOU
1♣	1H 21	1H 26	___ 31	1H 36
1◊	1H 22	1H 27	___ 32	1H 37
1♡	4H 23	3NT 28	___ 33	3H 38
1♠	1NT 24	3S 29	___ 34	2C 39
1NT	2D 25	3NT 30	___ 35	2C 40

	K953	K7	85	AK953
	A74	KJ83	A84	6
	76	J4	A972	AJ105
	J1053	AJ753	J1064	A75
PARTNER	YOU	YOU	YOU	YOU
1♣	*1S* 41	*1S* 46	*1H* 51	*1H* 56
1◇	*1S* 42	*1S* 47	*1H* 52	*1H* 57
1♡	*2H*	*1NT* 43	*2NT* 48	*3H* 53	*2 rebid* 58
1♠	*2S* 44	*3S* 49	*3S* 54	*2C* 59
1NT	*2C* 45	*2H* 50	*2C* 55	*2C* 60

III. Hand Evaluation

What would you call as South in the following situations? You are playing IMPs, none vulnerable.

Q105
KQJ7
764
864

WEST	NORTH	EAST	SOUTH
--	1♡	Pass	2♡
Pass	3♡	Pass	___ 61

QJ7
76
J8642
A65

WEST	NORTH	EAST	SOUTH
--	1NT (15-17)	Pass	
			___
			62

1073
Q5
K94
AKJ54

WEST	NORTH	EAST	SOUTH
--	1♠	Pass	2♣
Pass	2♡	Pass	3♠
Pass	4◇	Pass	
			___
			63

J
Q73
K853
J9542

WEST	NORTH	EAST	SOUTH
--	1♡	Pass	2♡
Pass	2NT	Pass	
			___
			64

A864
Q953
87
864

WEST	NORTH	EAST	SOUTH
--	1♡	Pass	2♡
Pass	Pass	Dbl	Pass
3♣	Pass	Pass	_____
			65

A54
853
9542
864

WEST	NORTH	EAST	SOUTH
--	2NT (21-22)	Pass	_____
			66

KJ8
10753
AQ4
Q105

WEST	NORTH	EAST	SOUTH
--	1◇	1♠	_____
			67

A76
J964
A7
K653

WEST	NORTH	EAST	SOUTH
--	1◊	1♠	
			___
			68

K6
AK103
Q1064
AQ7

WEST	NORTH	EAST	SOUTH
--	--	--	1◊
Pass	1NT	Pass	
			___
			69

QJ65
KJ7
AQ4
QJ2

WEST	NORTH	EAST	SOUTH
--	1NT (16-18)	Pass	2♣
Pass	2◊	Pass	
			___
			70

KJ64
KQ76
753
87

WEST	NORTH	EAST	SOUTH
—	1♦	Pass	1♡
Pass	1♠	Pass	2♠
Pass	3♠	Pass	____
			71

9643
KJ7
K76
Q86

WEST	NORTH	EAST	SOUTH
—	1♡	2♣	2♡
3♣	3♦	Pass	____
			72

KQ76
973
A865
A6

WEST	NORTH	EAST	SOUTH
—	—	—	1♦
Pass	1♠	Pass	2♠
Pass	3♣	Pass	____
			73

K75
74
KQ4
KQJ65

WEST	NORTH	EAST	SOUTH
—	—	—	1♣
Pass	1♡	1♠	1NT
Pass	2NT	Pass	———
			74

8653
KJ8642
A
Q7

WEST	NORTH	EAST	SOUTH
1♠	Dbl	3♠	———
			75

1   Pass   It beats us why anybody would want to open this junk. The object of the game is still to win tricks, isn't it? Yes, you have a spade suit — but can you afford to rebid 1♠ after 1♣-1♡?

2   Pass   We like a pass. A weak 2♡ opening is possible; however, this hand will make a good dummy for a spade or diamond contract.

3   1♠   So you've got only 10 points in high cards. You also have some playing tricks, 2½ defensive tricks and a comfortable rebid. Last time we looked, that's what an opening bid required.

4   Pass   Did we say this was a simple exercise? We think the best way to describe this hand is to pass and back in with a double or the Unusual Notrump. We hope the auction won't be up to 6♠ by the next round.

It's not terrible to open 2♡ and bid your clubs later, if you've discussed this concept with your partner.

5   Pass   Poor high cards and defense (strike one), long suit is ragged (strike two), rebid problems looming (strike three and out).

6   1♣   Why open 1◊ when you have no intention of rebidding 2♣ over a major-suit response? The only thing you might accomplish by opening 1◊ is losing a club fit.

7   1♠   The good old black two-suiter. At least one world champion of our acquaintance prefers a 1♣ opening, but we're unrepentant; we like 1♠ (except in an extreme case, which this isn't).

8   1◊   All we know is, Eddie Kantar once opened 1◊ on a hand like this in the Team Trials.

9   1♣   Rebid 1NT over a 1♠ response. 1◊ followed by a 2♣ rebid misdescribes the pattern *and* fails to limit the hand.

10   1♣   We still bid the longest suit first. We'd rather rebid 2♣ — or even 1NT — over a major-suit response than go the 1◊-2♣ route with a minimum hand.

11   1◇   This hand is strong enough to bid three times (for example, the auction: 1◇-1♠-2♣-2◇-2NT), so the 1◇ opening is okay. Some players might be willing to reverse, but it's not for us.

12   1♣   You must pass a 1NT response. But if partner plays it there and goes down, the opponents probably can make a heart partial.

13   1◇   With all primary values and *low* singleton spade, we'd rebid 2♣ over 1♠. With Q, Q10xx, AJ9x, KJ9x, we'd be willing to rebid 1NT and thus would open 1♣.

14   1◇   Over partner's 2♣, we can rebid 2♡, which is not a reverse after a two-level response.

15   2♣   Awkward, thy name is the big three-suiter short in spades. If you open 2♣, you may not have room to find your best trump suit. Partner will usually respond 2◇, and your 3◇ rebid will consume space and make him declarer in a diamond contract. (Here, at least, you have a five-card suit to rebid — things would be worse with a monster 1-4-4-4.) Still, there's nothing delicious about a 1◇ opening. The suspense of waiting for someone to bid is terrible. And can you ever convey the power of this hand after a one-bid?

       Our recommendation — open 2♣. If the opponents bid spades, you may be able to turn it to your advantage. Second choice: Take up another system.

16   2♣   No problem, especially since your long suit is a major.

17   1NT   Second choice is 1♡, but this requires a 2♣ rebid over a 1♠ response, because you are too good to rebid 1NT.

18   1NT   Slightly misshapen, but most of the values are in the short suits. Here's hoping you never pick up xx, AKJx, AKJxx, xx.

19   1♠

20   Pass   Unless your hero is Marty Bergen. Sorry, not enough imagination here (and not enough of a bank balance) for a 3♣ opening.

21   1♣ - 1♡

22   1♢ - 1♡

23   1♡ - 4♡

24   1♠ - 1NT

25   1NT - 2♣   Follow with 2♡ over 2♢, 4♡ over 2♡, and 3♡ over 2♠. If playing transfers, bid 2♢ and raise 2♡ to 3♡.

26   1♣ - 1♡

27   1♢ - 1♡   A 2NT response to 1♣ or 1♢ is acceptable and would be mandatory in some partnerships.

28   1♡ - 3♡   If forcing, or your conventional forcing raise.

29   1♠ - 2NT   If natural; otherwise 2♣.

30   1NT - 3NT   No need to seek a 4-4 heart fit with this much high-card strength.

31   1♣ - 1♢

32   1♢ - 2NT   Intending to bid 4♢ if partner raises to 3NT.

33   1♡ - 2♢

34   1♠ - 3NT

35   1NT - 4NT   Quantitative; however, if partner's notrump has a 16-point bottom, we'd take the pressure off him by bidding 6NT.

36   1♣ - 1♡

37   1♢ - 1♡   Not enough ammunition to bid 2♣, then hearts, then support diamonds.

38   1♡ - 2♣   Difficult. A 3♡ response, even if forcing, would suggest a balanced hand. A 3♠ splinter response, if available, would show this hand nicely.

39   1♠ - 2♣

40   1NT - 2♣   Or whatever conventional method you have going for you.

41   1♣ - 1♠

42   1◇ - 1♠

43   1♡ - 2♡   Opposite a five-card major opening, forget the spades.

44   1♠ - 2♠

45   1NT - Pass   Assuming 1NT shows any 15-17 points. Your game chances are too poor to bid 2♣, which suggests game interest. Opposite a sounder 15⁺-17 notrump, you could risk 2♣.

46   1♣ - 1♡

47   1◇ - 2♣

48   1♡ - 3♡   If forcing, or your own forcing raise.

49   1♠ - 2♣

50   1NT - 2♣   Or your conventional method.

51   1♣ - 1◇   A bit too strong for a single raise.

52   1◇ - 2◇

53   1♡ - 2♡

54   1♠ - 1NT

55   1NT - 2NT

56   1♣ - 1♠

57   1◇ - 2♠   Intending to support diamonds next.

58   1♡ - 1♠   Since the best strain is in doubt, go slowly.

59   1♠ - 3◇

60   1NT - 3♠   Or your conventional method.

61   Pass   The ♡J is a wasted card and the flat distribution ruins the value of your fourth trump. However, if you did bid game, you are not in terrible company. My editors and I disagree on this one.

62   Pass   Your long suit may be hard to establish. At IMPs, it's close.

63   4♠   Don't cooperate with bad trumps.

64   3♡   Since you have only three trumps, the value of your singleton spade goes down. The expected trump opening lead may be damaging. You would jump to 4♡ with J, Qxxx, Kxxx, Jxxx.

65   3♡   Your fourth trump lets you compete to the three level.

66   Pass   Partner's high cards are worth less because he can reach your hand only once to lead toward them. If vulnerable, risk 3NT.

67   2NT   If forcing, or 3NT. Be aggressive; your ♠KJ are worth an A-Q.

68   Dbl   If negative; otherwise bid 2♣. This time your 4 points in spades will produce only one trick. Be conservative unless partner can bid notrump or show extra strength.

69   3NT   Responder is marked with club length, and you have a fine club fit.

70   4NT   Give partner some leeway in slam decisions. You have too many jacks and queens to bid slam on your own. Also, if opener has the likely A-Q-x in hearts, your ♡J is a wasted point.

71   Pass   Your holding in partner's first suit is the worst, and your ♡Q may not be pulling its weight. You'd go on in a flash with a hand like: Kxxx, Axxx, Qxx, xx.

72   3♡   Your ♣Q isn't worth the cardboard it's printed on. Your diamond fit means slightly less than usual because 3◇ was the only game-try partner had available. Who knows what he has in diamonds?

73   4♠   You can cover partner's club losers, and your side card is an ace.

74   Pass   Your spade stopper will soon be dislodged, and your lack of aces means that the defenders have entries to set up their long suit.

75   6♡   Or 4NT. Partner is likely to be void in spades, which means his high-card values lie elsewhere. Slam is odds-on if he holds something like: --, Axxx, Jxxx, K10xxx, and he might have more!

Leading Questions

I. Basics

As West, what do you lead in these basic situations? All problems are at matchpoints, neither side vulnerable.

```
8652
K6
J1073                    _____
KJ2          76
```

WEST	NORTH	EAST	SOUTH
——	——	——	1♡
Pass	1♠	Pass	3♡
Pass	4♡	All Pass	


```
QJ93
AJ93
76                       _____
Q102         77
```

WEST	NORTH	EAST	SOUTH
——	——	——	1♡
Pass	1♠	Pass	2♣
All Pass			


```
83
Q1054
KJ92                     _____
A104         78
```

WEST	NORTH	EAST	SOUTH
——	——	——	1♡
Pass	1♠	Pass	1NT
Pass	2NT	All Pass	

AK
J108
KJ6
A10753   79

WEST	NORTH	EAST	SOUTH
1NT	Pass	2♣	2♠
All Pass			

J10
108542
Q93
753   80

WEST	NORTH	EAST	SOUTH
——	——	——	1NT
Pass	3NT	All Pass	

4
A842
Q10863
AJ5   81

WEST	NORTH	EAST	SOUTH
——	1♣	Pass	1♡
Pass	1♠	Pass	3♡ (forcing)
Pass	4♡	All Pass	

J98642
76
A64
76   82

WEST	NORTH	EAST	SOUTH
——	——	3♣	3♡
Pass	4♡	Dbl	All Pass

Q65
863
A6
AK752   83

WEST	NORTH	EAST	SOUTH
——	1♠	Pass	2◇
Pass	2♠	Pass	2NT
Pass	3NT	All Pass	

K5
9642
Q1082
A105   84

WEST	NORTH	EAST	SOUTH
——	——	——	1♣
Pass	1◇	Pass	1♡
Pass	2♡	Pass	3♡
Pass	4♡	All Pass	

9843
Q93
A1053
A5   85

WEST	NORTH	EAST	SOUTH
——	——	2◇ [1]	3♣
3◇	3♠	Pass	4♡
Pass	5♣	Pass	6♣
All Pass			

[1] Weak two-bid

II. Disasters

The following lead problems arose in international matches with IMP scoring. Again, you are West. However, this time we aren't asking you to pick the best lead. Instead, *choose the lead that preceded a disaster!*

95
842
8542
A973   ———
              86

WEST	NORTH	EAST	SOUTH
——	——	——	2♣
Pass	2♠	Pass	3♡
Pass	3♠	Pass	4♢
Pass	5♡	Pass	6♡
All Pass			

——
A753
875
J108754   ———
               87

WEST	NORTH	EAST	SOUTH
——	——	——	1♣ [1]
Pass	1♡ [2]	1♠	1NT
Pass	2♣	Pass	2♢
Pass	2♠	Pass	3NT
All Pass			

[1] 17+ points
[2] Six+ points, fewer than two controls (A=2, K=1)

3
A987
K952
9872   ___
             88

WEST	NORTH	EAST	SOUTH
——	Pass	Pass	1◊ [1]
Pass	1♡ [2]	Pass	2♠ [3]
Pass	3♠	Pass	4♠
Pass	5◊	Pass	6♠
All Pass			

[1] At least four diamonds, forcing
[2] Artificial negative
[3] Longer spades, strong

9
AQ543
K972
A97   ___
             89

WEST	NORTH	EAST	SOUTH
1♡	Pass	2♡	2♠
3♡	3♠	All Pass	

9874
Q8
A976
K86   ___
             90

WEST	NORTH	EAST	SOUTH
——	——	Pass	1♠
Pass	2♣	Dbl	Pass
2◊	4♠	All Pass	

1075
KQ762
——
Q10932   91

WEST	NORTH	EAST	SOUTH
——	2♣ 1	Pass	2◊ 2
Pass	3♣ 3	Pass	3NT
All Pass			

1 Minimum, long clubs
2 Artificial inquiry
3 No major, at most one suit besides clubs stopped

KJ1097
1087
9
9642   92

WEST	NORTH	EAST	SOUTH
——	3◊	Pass	6NT
All Pass			

98763
K3
K85
963   93

WEST	NORTH	EAST	SOUTH
——	——	——	1♣
Pass	1♠	Pass	3NT
Pass	4NT	Pass	5♠
Pass	7NT	All Pass	

J8
KQ973
AJ83
107   ——— 94

WEST	NORTH	EAST	SOUTH
Pass	Pass	Pass	1♠
2♡	2♠	3♡	4♠
All Pass			

984
AJ872
J75
A4   ——— 95

WEST	NORTH	EAST	SOUTH
——	——	——	1◇
1♡	2♣	4♡	4♠
All Pass			

III. Notable Leads

As West, what would you have led on these notable deals from actual play? IMP scoring, unless otherwise indicated.

43
A75
KQ103
10982   ——— 96

WEST	NORTH	EAST	SOUTH
Pass	1♡	Pass	1♠
Pass	2♣	Pass	Pass
2◇	2♠	3◇	4♠
Pass	Pass	Dbl	All Pass

87
J72
1092
K9865   97

WEST	NORTH	EAST	SOUTH
——	——	1♡	Dbl
Pass	2♡	3♡	3♠
Pass	4NT	Pass	5♣
Pass	6♠	Dbl	All Pass

J6543
K42
Q42
J2   98

WEST	NORTH	EAST	SOUTH
——	Pass	Pass	3NT [1]
All Pass			

[1] Solid minor, one side stopper

A54
AJ5
964
J852   99

WEST	NORTH	EAST	SOUTH
——	——	——	Pass
Pass	1◇	1♠	1NT
2♠	3◇	Pass	3NT
Dbl	All Pass		

J32
J97
K
AK10864   ____
                 100

WEST	NORTH	EAST	SOUTH
2♣	Dbl	Pass	3NT
All Pass			

AQ6
K1063
9854
86   ____
                 101

WEST	NORTH	EAST	SOUTH
Pass	Pass	Pass	1♡
Pass	2♣	Pass	2◇
Pass	2♠	Pass	3NT
All Pass			

4   Matchpoints
J10943
865
Q943   ____
                 102

WEST	NORTH	EAST	SOUTH
——	2♡ 1	Pass	4♠
All Pass			

1 Weak in spades or intermediate/strong in hearts

J86
A962
Q1072
J2   103

WEST	NORTH	EAST	SOUTH
Pass	Pass	2♡	2♠
4♡	4♠	5♡	Pass
Pass	5♠	All Pass	

J85
9
A10763
A986   104

WEST	NORTH	EAST	SOUTH
—	—	—	1♠
Pass	2♡	Pass	2♠
Pass	3♠	Pass	4♠
All Pass			

1073
53
KQ5
KJ743   105   Matchpoints

WEST	NORTH	EAST	SOUTH
—	—	Pass	1NT [1]
Pass	2♣	Pass	2♠
Pass	3NT	All Pass	

[1] 13-15

76   ♣2. The opponents have had a strong auction, and dummy's spades are a threat to provide discards. You must get busy, and clubs is the best hope for tricks.

77   ♣2. Dummy will usually be short in hearts, and you have possible heart tricks to protect. Even if the ♣Q would have been a trick, you'll break even by stopping some ruffs.

78   ♠8. The opponents have no extra high-card strength, and South's hearts won't come in. Play it passive. An aggressive diamond lead could give declarer his eighth trick.

79   ♣A, then another club. It's odd that East sold out so cheaply; a Stayman response normally suggests game interest. East probably has a bad 4-4-4-1 and was going to pass any rebid. When South overcalls and you hold the ♠AK, there is little danger of giving East ruffs with natural trump tricks.

80   ♠J. Try to hit East's long suit. Since you lack a side entry, you are unlikely to set up and cash hearts. However, if you play that a double by partner would have called for a spade lead, you might lead a heart, on the theory that his failure to double makes a spade lead less likely to succeed.

81   ♢6. Your hand is too strong for a singleton lead. Anyway, with four trumps and prospects of a successful forcing defense, it's far from clear that you want to ruff.

82   ♠J. East's double asks for an unusual lead. He should be void in spades. Lead the jack as a suit-preference signal to request a diamond return.

83   ♣2. There is no point in leading an honest ♣5, since East won't be involved in the defense. You hope declarer will think it's safe to knock out the ♢A instead of (successfully) developing spades.

84   ♡2. Stay away from the desperation lead of the ♠K when the situation is far from desperate. The opponents have struggled into game, and you have promising defense, including four trumps.

85   ♠9. South is surely void in diamonds. A spade lead will work in two cases: East has a singleton and gets a ruff when you win the trump ace; or you kill dummy with a second spade lead and preserve a late heart trick. The full deal is:

AQJ72
765
872
Q9

9843		106
Q93		J4
A1053		KQJ964
A5		632

K5
AK1082
—
KJ10874

86   In the 1953 Bermuda Bowl, West for Sweden led a trump. The U.S. declarer drew trumps, threw dummy's clubs away on the diamonds and conceded the ♠A. In the replay the defenders managed to cash their aces against the same contract.

KQ1074
10653
—
KQJ2

95		A832
842		9
8542		10973
A973		10654

J6
AKQJ7
AKQJ6
8

87   In the 1965 Bermuda Bowl, an American West tried the ♣J, which crashed East's queen and gave declarer his ninth trick. In the other room, the U.S. contract was 2NT.

```
                    109854
                    Q42
                    J10
                    K93
    —                           QJ763
    A753                        986
    875                         AQ64
    J108754                     Q
                    AK2
                    KJ10
                    K932
                    A62
```

88   In the 1958 Bermuda Bowl, West for the U.S. laid down the ♡A. His trump shift was too late — the Italian declarer ruffed two diamonds in dummy and threw one on the ♣A. At the other table the U.S. N-S stopped in 4♠.

```
                    654
                    10542
                    7
                    AJ1065
    3                           1072
    A987                        QJ6
    K952                        Q1086
    9872                        Q43
                    AKQJ98
                    K3
                    AJ43
                    K
```

Since West held the ◇K, he might have inferred that North's 5◇ cuebid showed a singleton. That would have made a trump lead a standout.

89   In the 1975 Bermuda Bowl round-robin, U.S. vs. Italy, a U.S. West led
the ◇2. Declarer let it ride to his queen and made his contract. In the
other room the Italians made 3♡ on the E-W cards.

<pre>
                              A65
                              1092
                              A8
                              QJ862
            9   J1072
            AQ543   K87
            K972   J1065
            A97   105
                              KQ843
                              J6
                              Q43
                              K43
</pre>

90   In the 1975 Bermuda Bowl round-robin, U.S. vs. France, an American
West led the ♡Q, giving the contract. In the replay West led a trump
against 4♠ for down one.

<pre>
                              A1052
                              976
                              8
                              AQ954
            9874   —
            Q8   A543
            A976   KJ1054
            K86   10732
                              KQJ63
                              KJ102
                              Q32
                              J
</pre>

An expert panel considered this problem and overwhelmingly preferred
to lead the ♡Q, vindicating the U.S. West.

91 In the 1974 Bermuda Bowl, West for the U.S. picked the ♡6, and the Italian South made his game. In the other room 3NT was played by North, and *East* led a heart for down two.

```
                        86
                        J10
                        A1043
                        AKJ75
        1075                          QJ42
        KQ762                         954
        --                           KQ9762
        Q10932                        --
                        AK93
                        A83
                        J85
                        864
```

92 In the 1961 Bermuda Bowl, West for Italy led the ◇9! The French declarer happily covered with dummy's 10 and tabled his cards, claiming the slam. That meant +990 to France and one embarrassed Italian bridge player.

```
                        8
                        Q5
                        K1087432
                        QJ5
        KJ1097                        542
        1087                          K9643
        9                            AJ5
        9642                          107
                        AQ63
                        AJ2
                        Q6
                        AK83
```

In the replay, Italy's N-S reached 3NT, against which West found a good heart lead. East eventually got two diamonds and three hearts to beat the game. Luckily for Italy, their lead at this point was so big that the loss was affordable.

93   In the 1969 European Championship, West thought that a club lead into declarer's "solid suit" would be safe. It wasn't.

                              AKQ1052
                              985
                              QJ96
                              --
        98763   4
        K3   Q10742
        K85   10743
        963   Q104
                              J
                              AJ6
                              A2
                              AKJ8752

94   In the 1970 International Team Trials, West tried the imaginative lead of the ♡9. In a galaxy far, far away, South would have had a singleton heart and the ◊K, and East would have held the ♡A and the doubleton ◊Q. As it was, declarer won the first trick with the ♡J and made his contract.

                              764
                              J4
                              K96
                              KJ863
        J8   932
        KQ973   1086
        AJ83   10742
        107   AQ4
                              AKQ105
                              A52
                              Q5
                              952

95   In the 1970 Tournament of Champions at Deauville, France, West (we won't tell you his name, but he's a famous actor-bridge player) led the ♣4. With spades splitting 3-3, the contract was suddenly unbeatable.

```
                              QJ3
                              9
                              2
                              KQJ109632
         984                                  1062
         AJ872                                KQ10653
         J75                                  A98
         A4                                   5
                              AK75
                              4
                              KQ10643
                              87
```

96   In the 1976 Team Trials, West, Ron Von der Porten, diagnosed East's club shortness from the N-S bidding and the double of 4♠. He therefore led the ♣10 and subsequently gave East a club ruff for the setting trick. Note that a trump lead would also have been successful, because East could win and switch to a club himself.

```
                              1087
                              KQ63
                              6
                              AKQ54
         43                                   AK6
         A75                                  109842
         KQ103                                9874
         10982                                7
                              QJ952
                              J
                              AJ52
                              J63
```

97　East probably has a void and a sure trick. If he's void in clubs, you can lead any club effectively. If East has a diamond void and the ♣A, you must lead the ♣K (or a diamond) to beat the contract.

```
                        A1054
                        A3
                        AJ8543
                        J
        87                              J2
        J72                             KQ109865
        1097                            —
        K9865                           A732
                        KQ963
                        4
                        KQ62
                        Q104
```

Perhaps West should analyze his partner's void correctly. North must have a distributional hand to drive to slam — he can't have that much in high cards. Perhaps he has four spades and a six-card minor. But when you hold five clubs, and South has promised club support, North's long suit can't be clubs.

In a 1970 match between the Aces and the Omar Sharif Circus, both Wests led a low club against 6♠.

98   Against gambling-style bidding, it often pays to lay down an ace on opening lead to keep the defense flexible. Without an ace, make the most aggressive lead available. On this deal, from the 1971 Spingold, Edgar Kaplan led the ♡2 for down three.

```
                        AK10
                        Q5
                        108763
                        1063
        J6543                           972
        K42                             AJ10973
        Q54                             A92
        J2                              7
                        Q8
                        86
                        KJ
                        AKQ9854
```

99   In the 1973 Trials, Mike Becker, West, judged that East had a two-suited hand to explain his overcall, with obviously skimpy high-card strength. In that case, East had to hold clubs, since he would have tried 2◊, a Michaels cuebid, with spades and hearts. West therefore followed his double with the ♣2 lead and beat the contract two tricks.

```
                        3
                        Q763
                        AKQJ85
                        63
        A54                             K10972
        AJ5                             92
        964                             3
        J852                            AQ1094
                        QJ86
                        K1084
                        1072
                        K7
```

100   In a Sunday Times Pairs in London, Giorgio Belladonna found the
       remarkable lead of the ♣10! Declarer duly went down two.

                                AQ95
                                KQ65
                                Q853
                                9
         J32   10876
         J97   10843
         K   A109
         AK10864   73
                                K4
                                A2
                                J7642
                                QJ52

101   In the 1976 Bermuda Bowl, Arturo Franco for Italy led the ♠A and
       continued spades for down one. 3NT also went down at the other table,
       but North was declarer and East led a spade.

                                10532
                                A7
                                3
                                AJ10752
         AQ6   J9874
         K1063   842
         9854   K62
         86   Q9
                                K
                                QJ95
                                AQJ107
                                K43

102   In the 1970 World Open Pairs, Eddie Kantar made the good decision to lead a club — holding 4♠ to five was worth a big score. Kantar drew the inference that South must have a good heart holding; otherwise, how did he know that North had spades? So it was a good time to avoid the routine ♡J lead.

	QJ10875	
	A75	
	J10	
	K3	
4		962
J10943		82
865		K943
Q954		AJ86
	AK3	
	KQ6	
	AQ72	
	1072	

103   In the 1958 Bermuda Bowl, Sidney Silodor astutely led the ♡9 to East's queen. If East had returned a low diamond, declarer surely would have gone wrong. But East laid down the ◇A, and Silodor's brilliance was wasted.

	K93	
	8	
	J653	
	AQ1095	
J86		10
A962		KQ10753
Q1072		A84
J2		873
	AQ7542	
	J4	
	K9	
	K64	

In the other room, the U.S. bought the deal for 4♠.

104   At a crucial point in the 1968 Open Team Olympiad final, U.S. against Italy, Camillo Pabis-Ticci led the ♣A. Then came another club for a ruff, a diamond to the ace and a club ruff. West still had a trump trick for down two.

```
                        K6
                        AJ632
                        8
                        QJ752
        J85                             Q9
        9                               Q10875
        A10763                          J9542
        A986                            10
                        A107432
                        K4
                        KQ
                        K43
```

In the replay the U.S. West led the ♡9, and Italy's declarer made four.

105   In the 1978 World Mixed Pairs, Barry Crane went against the field by leading the ◇K. Just avoiding a club lead guaranteed him a good matchpoint score; but South later misguessed and went down in his contract, giving Crane a top.

```
                        K4
                        QJ72
                        A7
                        A10862
        1073                            Q652
        53                              10986
        KQ5                             J1096
        KJ743                           9
                        AJ98
                        AK4
                        8432
                        Q5
```

Why didn't West lead his five-card suit? We don't know — that's what made him Barry Crane.

Preempts

I. Do You or Don't You?

What is your action as dealer at IMPs with neither side vulnerable?

Q105	J5	8	87	Q105
K76	J4	J74	764	Q6
QJ108654	Q1086532	KQJ9762	AKQ9753	KJ97532
--	76	54	Q	Q
_____	_____	_____	_____	_____
106	107	108	109	110

Dealer, at your right, passes. What is your action at IMPs with neither side vulnerable?

KJ97632
A75
7
J5   _____ 111

What is your action after two passes? IMPs, neither side vulnerable.

K105
8
Q1097542
Q3   _____ 112

What is your action after three passes? IMPs, neither side vulnerable.

76	8	KJ6	7
7	A6	Q8	AKQ10863
AKJ9653	AKJ9653	KQJ9653	KJ3
Q84	Q65	A	K4

| 113 | 114 | 115 | 116 |

II. Partner Preempts

Partner deals and opens 3◊, and the next player passes. What is your action at IMPs with neither side vulnerable?

AK9653	Q53	K10
AK4	A83	A964
Q4	Q76	K105
76	J942	AQ32

| 117 | 118 | 119 |

AKQ10654	Q6	8
A8	AQ109653	A863
--	7	K953
A763	A64	J1052

| 120 | 121 | 122 |

7	A86	A
AK64	AK63	KQJ9653
Q864	5	4
AK53	AQ642	KJ105

| 123 | 124 | 125 |

III. Partner Responds to Your Preempt

You deal and open 3◊ at IMPs with neither side vulnerable. Partner responds 3♡. What is your action?

7	87	K105	87	84
J5	Q94	74	7	5
AJ107543	AJ107542	KJ109652	KJ107532	KJ109653
J105	3	7	QJ7	J92
___	___	___	___	___
126	127	128	129	130

IV. An Opponent Preempts

Dealer, at your right, opens 3♣. What is your action at IMPs with neither side vulnerable?

K5	KQ10653	K4	A853	A63
AKJ963	A65	AKQ1074	KJ76	KQ6
A53	Q853	AQ53	AQ54	AKJ2
43	—	6	6	K104
___	___	___	___	___
131	132	133	134	135

65	K	AJ54	J6	A4
A7	AJ5	4	QJ1086542	KQ953
AKQ10764	KQJ753	AK42	K	AKJ653
K4	KQ6	Q1075	75	—
___	___	___	___	___
136	137	138	139	140

Dealer, at your left, opens 3♡, passed to you. What is your action at IMPs with neither side vulnerable?

AJ9543	KQJ1075	KQ63	76	A65
Q7	76	64	K75	K64
K1065	AK6	A853	AKJ853	Q96
6	A5	KJ5	K4	K942
141	142	143	144	145

V. Partner Overcalls a Preempt

IMPs, neither side vulnerable. Dealer, at your left, opens 3◇. Partner overcalls 3♡. What is your action?

K643	A953	AK64	964	Q864
Q6	Q6	Q7	K6	AJ4
J75	J64	J64	K94	7
Q532	KJ63	AQJ8	A8652	AK753
146	147	148	149	150

IMPs, neither side vulnerable. Dealer, at your right, opens 3♣. After two passes partner reopens with 3♠. What is your action?

87	K432	A94	K954	--
J943	A96	A75	KJ	KJ953
K65	974	AQ104	AKJ7	J10765
KQ93	Q76	953	1064	A54
151	152	153	154	155

106   Pass. We tend not to preempt when our hand would make a good dummy for a contract in *either* major suit.

107   Pass. We can stand the diamond suit — barely — for a preempt, but not with 7-2-2-2 distribution as well.

108   Open 3◊. A textbook preempt.

109   Pass or open 1◊. Avoid a preempt with a solid suit.

110   Pass. Too many defensive values to preempt, plus tolerance for both majors.

111   Pass. This is a poor preempt for several reasons: your suit is ragged; one opponent has passed, so there is less reason for aggressive tactics; you have the ranking suit and can outbid the opponents in a competitive auction.

112   Open 3◊. With partner a passed hand, you need not fear missing a spade fit.

113   Pass. You have much more to lose than to gain by opening.

114   Open 3◊. A fourth-hand preempt is constructive. You would like to hear partner try 3NT with a side stopper or two.

115   Open 1◊. Bid normally. You have no reason to open at the three level with this much strength.

116   Open 4♡. This would be unthinkable in first or second seat, but now you can bid the most likely contract while trying to shut out the spades.

117   Bid 3♠, forcing.

118   Bid 3NT. This is a good tactical shot. Almost surely, the opponents can make game.

119   Bid 3NT to make.

120   Bid 3NT. This may be the only makable game.

121   Pass. You can't afford to bid 3♡, which is forcing.

122   Bid 5◊. The advance sacrifice will force the opponents to start looking for their best contract at the five level.

123   Bid 4NT, Blackwood.

124   Bid 5◊. A poor player would bid 3NT, but partner's long suit will be useful only if diamonds are trumps. Your top cards will make the diamond game a good spot.

125   Bid 4♡. (A playable method is to treat a jump in a new suit as an asking bid. If responder held AKQ, xxx, Ax, AKxxx, he could learn if opener had a heart control.)

126   Bid 4♡.

127   Bid 4♣, an advance cuebid. You could hardly have a better supporting hand for hearts after a 3◊ opening.

128   Bid 3♠, which promises a stopper. Perhaps partner will wish to bid 3NT. Of course, you could have heart support and a spade control (see #127), but then you'll support hearts next.

129   Bid 3NT. You can hardly have *both* black suits stopped, and you would bid 3♠ with a spade stopper but no club stopper. Therefore, this bid implies something in clubs.

130   Bid 4◊. What else?

131   Bid 3♡. This is a dangerous action. However, you must assume that your partner has a few points, otherwise you will be stolen blind.

132   Bid 3♠. Although you are light in high cards, the club void makes it advisable to act.

133   Bid 4♡.

134   Double. Minimum in high cards, but perfect shape.

135   Double, planning to convert a 3♡ or 3♠ response to 3NT. If partner's hand is unbalanced, he can insist on a suit contract.

136   Bid 3NT. This time partner should sit for notrump, unless his hand is wildly unbalanced.

137   Bid 3NT. Too good to overcall 3◇.

138   Pass. A double would be for takeout, and partner would bid hearts.

139   Pass. Any heart bid would promise high-card values.

140   4♣, suggesting a two-suited hand.

141   Bid 3♠. You must lighten up on all your balancing actions.

142   Bid 4♠.

143   Double.

144   Bid 3NT.

145   Pass.

146   Pass.

147   Bid 4♡.

148   Bid 5♡, committing to slam if partner has a diamond control.

149   Bid 3NT.

150   Bid 4◇.

151   Pass. Don't get angry and bid 3NT to punish partner for not reopening with a double.

152   Pass. Partner has won his gamble by balancing. Don't hang him. Your ♣Q is probably worthless. Yes, game is possible, but not at all probable.

153   Bid 4♠.

154   Bid 4♣, showing a strong hand with spade support, provided your partner won't expect more than fourth-round control. Some scientists might risk a 4◇ bid instead; with a good hand and a diamond suit, you might have overcalled earlier.

155   Bid 4♡. This may be your best percentage action, because if you're right, you score a game. Passing 3♠ could also work, especially when you avoid going for a number. Last, and surely least, is the 4♣ cuebid, asking partner to choose a red suit when he is psychic enough to read your mind.

QUICK QUIZ

Systems Around the World

Match the following noted partnerships with their bidding systems.

156	Camillo Pabis-Ticci/Massimo D'Alelio	*Standard American*
157	Howard Schenken-Peter Leventritt	*Two-way two-bids*
158	Pietro Forquet-Eugenio Chiaradia	*Watch your step*
159	Bob Hamman-Bobby Wolff	*Ultimate Club*
160	Omar Sharif-Paul Chemla	*Schenken Club*
161	Fred Hamilton-Ira Rubin	*Roman Club*
162	Bill Root-Alvin Roth	*Aces Club*
163	Jim Jacoby-Bobby Wolff	*Acol*
164	Mike Becker-Ron Rubin	*Roth-Stone*
165	Edgar Kaplan-Norman Kay	*Orange Club*
166	Charles Goren-Helen Sobel	*Cowardly K-S*
167	Jeff Meckstroth-Eric Rodwell	*Super Precision*
168	Terence Reese-Boris Schapiro	*Neapolitan Club*
169	Giorgio Belladonna-Walter Avarelli	*Little Roman Club (Arno)*
170	Zia Mahmood-Anybody he plays with	*Natural, Five-Card Majors*

156   Pabis-Ticci and D'Alelio used the Little Roman Club (also known as Arno).

157   Schenken-Leventritt employed Schenken's Big Club.

158   Forquet-Chiaradia used Chiaradia's Neapolitan Club.

159   Hamman-Wolff play the Aces Club, which is based on Blue Team.

160   Sharif-Chemla use natural bidding with five-card majors.

161   Hamilton and Rubin utilized Rubin's two-way two-bids.

162   Root-Roth used Roth-Stone, of course.

163   Jacoby-Wolff used the Orange Club in the early days of the Dallas Aces.

164   Becker-Rubin employ the Ultimate Club, a complex relay system.

165   Kaplan-Kay use "Cowardly K-S" (weak notrumps not vulnerable only).

166   Goren-Sobel played the natural system that evolved into Standard American.

167   Meckstroth and Rodwell play their own version of Super Precision.

168   Reese-Schapiro usually played Acol.

169   Belladonna-Avarelli played the Roman Club.

170   Zia's partners must watch their step, since he is known for his tricky bids.

Answers First!

Part 1 (Time limit: 5 seconds per question!)

Scoreboard

Tournament Directors	Bridge and Baseball	Winners	Conventions	Opening Bids	Coups
171	176	181	186	191	196
172	177	182	187	192	197
173	178	183	188	193	198
174	179	184	189	194	199
175	180	185	190	195	200

Tournament Directors

171 National director known for his omnipresent bow tie.

172 Dictum that advises you to always accept a lead out of turn.

173 National director who married Goren's favorite partner.

174 National director nicknamed for Telly Savalas TV character.

175 His "fabulous Uncle Al" was a famed TD with a stentorian voice.

Bridge and Baseball

176 Two-base hit or responsive.

177 Two suits you'll find on a baseball field.

178 Bridge/baseball play, and you also do it to a tube of toothpaste.

179 Houston ballplayer probably uses this convention over opponent's 1NT opening.

180 This Seventies Oriole outfielder's name means a holding of just one card in a suit.

Winners

181 All-time leader in McKenney Trophy wins with eight.

182 At Winnipeg in 1985, this world champion set an all-time record for masterpoints won at an NABC.

183 ACBL named him top performer of the double decade 1957-1977.

184 In 1957 he simultaneously held the Vanderbilt, Spingold, Chicago, Mixed Teams and Men's Teams titles.

185 These celebrated visitors to America won the Men's Pairs at the 1971 Spring NABC in Atlanta.

Conventions

186 Three-time world champion who developed the convention that bears Sam Stayman's name.

187 Convention that will get you from the airport to your hotel.

188 "Jordan," a 2NT response to show a limit raise over a takeout double, was actually originated by this player.

189   Response to 1NT that may have been used in the Roman Coliseum.

190   Early ace-asking variation that reveals which ace is missing when the partnership has three.

Opening Bids

191   The 1◊ opening in this system is often characterized as "nebulous."

192   Blue Team Club opening that shows 17-24 points and some 4-4-4-1 distribution.

193   Correct opening bid with QJ10976542, A, AKQ, --.

194   Cornerstones of this system are the Mexican 2◊ and Dynamic Notrump openings.

195   In this famous player's system, opening bids at the three level were strong.

Coups

196   Simple holdup with an A-J tenace is named for old English watering place.

197   Famed California prison lends its name to this illegal or unethical play.

198   French term for securing a ruff with a low trump means "coup in passing."

199   Strictly speaking, a "coup" is defined as this type of play.

200   Play you accomplish if you ruff two winning cards to reach a trump coup position.

Tournament Directors

171 Who is Maury Braunstein?

172 What is Goldwater's Rule? (Proposed by TD Harry Goldwater — "If he doesn't know whose lead it is, he probably doesn't know what to lead.")

173 Who is Al Sobel?

174 Who is Bill (Kojak) Schoder?

175 Who is Jerry Machlin?

Bridge and Baseball

176 What is a double?

177 What are clubs and diamonds?

178 What is a squeeze?

179 What is Astro?

180 Who is Ken Singleton?

Winners

181 Who is Charles Goren?

182 Who is Eric Rodwell?

183 Who is Norman Kay?

184 Who is John Crawford?

185 Who are Giorgio Belladonna-Benito Garozzo?

Conventions

186   Who is George Rapee?

187   What is a transfer?

188   Who is Alan Truscott?

189   What is Gladiator?

190   What is Roman Blackwood?

Opening Bids

191   What is Precision?

192   What is 2◊?

193   What is 5♠?

194   What is Romex?

195   Who is P. Hal Sims?

Coups

196   What is a Bath Coup?

197   What is an Alcatraz Coup?

198   What is a *coup en passant*?

199   What is a trump coup?

200   What is a double grand coup?

Answers First!

Part 2 (Time limit: 10 seconds per question.)

Bridge and Chess	Bermuda Bowl	Doubles	Political Arena	Books	Famous Disasters
201	206	211	216	221	226
202	207	212	217	222	227
203	208	213	218	223	228
204	209	214	219	224	229
205	210	215	220	225	230

Bridge and Chess

201   Game more likely to produce child prodigies.

202   Computer software is far more advanced in this game.

203   Bridge expert who drew at lightning chess with Tigran Petrosian when the then-world champion spotted him a knight.

204   Chess champions who recently made news by playing bridge between matches.

205   Magazine that once had world chess champions Emanuel Lasker and Jose Capablanca as contributing editors.

Bermuda Bowl

206 Silver Anniversary Bermuda Bowl was held on this island.

207 Country with the most second-place finishes in Bermuda Bowl.

208 Last woman player to represent the U.S. in the Bermuda Bowl.

209 In 1970 he captained U.S. to its first Bermuda Bowl win since 1954.

210 Number of times Alvin Roth has played for the U.S. in the Bermuda Bowl.

Doubles

211 After an opposing overcall, it shows three cards in partner's (responder's) suit.

212 It shows game interest when the only suit bid available would be strictly competitive.

213 If the opponents redouble this tactical double, you'll run like a cowardly primate.

214 Strange double that suggests an *inability* to beat the opponents' slam contract.

215 After 1NT-3NT, it asks for a club lead — but if responder had used Stayman, it would ask for a diamond lead.

Political Arena

216 Chinese head of state who was "Bridge Personality of the Year" in 1980.

217 U.S. President who, according to Oswald Jacoby, played bridge at almost the expert level.

218 A federal judge, she authored a noted book on conventions.

219 Famed bridge authority who devoted his later years to international politics and the quest for world peace.

220 This nationally-syndicated political columnist is a staunch bridge advocate.

Books

221 Latest edition of this bible by "Mr. Bridge" was published in 1985.

222 Hugh Kelsey made a terrific debut with this 1966 classic.

223 Darvas-Hart fantasy in which cards come alive, considered by many as all-time greatest bridge book.

224 1979 Kelsey-Ottlik work added abstruse new dimensions to the play of the hand.

225 BLUE was the mnemonic for squeeze principles in this book.

Famous Disasters

226 Year in which U.S. Bermuda Bowl team found itself down 124-6 after 32 deals in the final vs. Italy.

227 An asking-bid mixup late in the 1937 World Championship final cost them a grand slam and contributed to their divorce.

228 After going down in a cold 4♡ redoubled in the 1963 Bermuda Bowl, this player never again represented his country in the World Championship.

229 Record-breaking set taken by Russell-Harkavy in 1965 U.S. Team Trials.

230 Charles Dornbush misplayed this suit combination to lose his 7♡ contract and the 1943 Spingold.

Bridge and Chess

201   What is chess?

202   What is chess?

203   Who was Oswald Jacoby?

204   Who are Viktor Korchnoi and Anatoly Karpov?

205   What is *The Bridge World*?

Bermuda Bowl

206   What is Bermuda?

207   What is the United States?

208   Who is Dorothy Truscott?

209   Who is Oswald Jacoby?

210   What is three?

Doubles

211   What is a support double?

212   What is a maximal double?

213   What is the striped-tail ape double?

214   What is a negative slam double?

215   What is the Fisher double?

Political Arena

216   Who is Deng Xiaoping?

217   Who is Dwight D. Eisenhower?

218   Who is Amalya Kearse?

219   Who is Ely Culbertson?

220   Who is James J. Kilpatrick?

Books

221   What is *Goren's Contract Bridge Complete*?

222   What is *Killing Defense at Bridge*?

223   What is *Right Through the Pack*?

224   What is *Adventures in Card Play*?

225   What is *Bridge Squeezes Complete*? (Clyde Love was the author.)

Famous Disasters

226   What is 1973?

227   Who are Ely and Jo Culbertson?

228   Who is Eugenio Chiaradia?

229   What is 3200?

230   What is A-K-J-10-x-x opposite x-x?

To Describe a Hand — Opener's Problems

I.

Plan how you would conduct the auction as opening bidder on the following hands.

> 93
> AK4
> AJ72
> AQJ3

You open 1♣, and if partner responds . . .

1◊, you'll call	_____	231
1♡, you'll call	_____	232
1♠, you'll call	_____	233
1NT, you'll call	_____	234
2♣, you'll call	_____	235
2NT, you'll call	_____	236
3♣ (limit), you'll call	_____	237

AQ953
K43
4
AJ72

You open 1♠, and if partner responds . . .

1NT, you'll call   _____ 238

2♣, you'll call   _____ 239

2◊, you'll call   _____ 240

2♡, you'll call   _____ 241

2♠, you'll call   _____ 242

2NT (natural), you'll call   _____ 243

3◊, you'll call   _____ 244

3♡, you'll call   _____ 245

3♠ (limit), you'll call   _____ 246

3NT, you'll call   _____ 247

6
AQ5
KJ9653
AK2

You open 1◇, and if partner responds . . .

AKJ
4
Q753
AJ652

You open 1♣, and if partner responds . . .

1◇, you'll call _____ 255

1♡, you'll call _____ 256

1♠, you'll call _____ 257

1NT, you'll call _____ 258

2♣, you'll call _____ 259

2♡, you'll call _____ 260

2NT, you'll call _____ 261

3♣ (limit), you'll call _____ 262

A932
3
Q9632
AK10

You open 1◊, and if partner responds . . .

1♡, you'll call   _____ 263

1♠, you'll call   _____ 264

1NT, you'll call   _____ 265

2♣, you'll call   _____ 266

2◊, you'll call   _____ 267

2NT, you'll call   _____ 268

3◊ (limit), you'll call   _____ 269

K4
AK8652
AQ63
6

You open 1♡, and if partner responds . . .

1♠, you'll call _____ 270

1NT, you'll call _____ 271

2♣, you'll call _____ 272

2◊, you'll call _____ 273

2♡, you'll call _____ 274

2♠, you'll call _____ 275

2NT (natural), you'll call _____ 276

3♡ (limit), you'll call _____ 277

Q
K93
AQ63
K10852

You open 1♣, and if partner responds . . .

KQ54
AJ53
J532
A

You open 1◊, and if partner responds ....

231   3◊   Maybe a slight underbid, but the hand has plenty of losers. If responder now tries 3♠, bid 3NT; if he says 3♡ or 4♣, you may bid 5◊, hoping there is no trump loser in addition to two spades.

232   2◊   Planning to support hearts next.

233   2NT

234   3NT   Responder usually has a little extra for a 1NT response to 1♣.

235   2◊   Don't get starry-eyed with your 19 points. If partner returns to 3♣, try 3♡ and quit if he repeats clubs again. You may have too many losers for an 11-trick contract, and 3NT is likely to be a good spot only if partner can bid it.

236   4NT   A quantitative slam try.

237   3◊   You are going to game or slam.

238   2♣

239   3♣

240   2♠

241   3♡

242   Pass   It's tempting to bid 3♣, since game will have a good chance if responder has a suitable maximum. However, partners seldom produce exactly what you need.

243   3♣

244   3NT   Doesn't promise a balanced hand.

245 3♠ Awkward. You can't afford a raise to 4♡ — responder might pass. If he bids 3NT over 3♠, showing a strong balanced hand, you can bid 4♣, planning to bid 6♡ next to *invite seven*. If responder rebids 4♡ over 3♠, you'll cuebid 5♣ on the way to 6♡. If he raises 3♠ to 4♠, suggesting that his jump shift was based on a spade fit, you'll Blackwood into a heart slam or grand slam.

246 4♠

247 4♣ A club slam is possible. If responder has an average hand or no club fit, you hope he will return to 4♠.

248 3♣ Planning to support hearts next. The slight overbid in high cards is justified by the heart fit. Second choice: 2♣.

249 2♣ 3♢ is reasonable, but the suit is ragged. 2♣ is flexible. You can bid 2NT over 2♠, bid 3♢ over 2♡, and gamble 3NT over 2♢. If responder passes 2♣, so what?

250 3♢ You hope that if partner has a close decision, he will pass with a poor diamond fit. 2♣ is reasonable but riskier here — responder's hand is limited and he probably has club length.

251 2♡ Planning to support clubs next. When you bid out your pattern like this, responder can tell how well the partnership hands fit.

252 3♣ Planning to bid 3♡ over a return to 3♢. Responder can then bid 3NT with a hand like Kxx, xx, Axxx, xxxx. This sequence also gets you to 6♢ if responder has a magic xxx, Kxx, Axxx, Qxx. The alternative is simply to blast into 5♢, giving the defenders no help.

253 4NT

254 3♢ Forcing.

255 3♢ Slight overbid.

256 1NT Close second choice: 1♠, treating those spades as a four-card suit. This is an unbalanced hand, after all.

257   2♠   Extra high cards but only three trumps. Also, partner will have to ruff hearts with high trumps.

258   2♣   Responder surely has three clubs.

259   2◇   Game may be an excellent proposition if partner has something in diamonds; e.g., xx, xxx, KJx, Kxxxx or Qx, xxx, Kxx, Kxxxx.

260   2NT   Opener could also rebid 2♠ to show a concentration of values.

261   3◇   If responder now bids 3♡, you can return to 3NT.

262   3◇   Game is likely. Slam is even possible. If responder bids 3♡ over 3◇, you will bid 3NT. If responder bids 3NT, you will pass. But if partner bids 4◇, you are on your way to slam.

263   1♠

264   2♠

265   2♣   Better than 2◇ when your diamonds are so ragged. Responder is marked with club length.

266   3♣

267   Pass

268   3♣   Most flexible bid to find out if you belong in 3NT or 5◇. Over partner's 3◇, you can rebid 3♠ to show the heart shortage.

269   3♠

270   2◇

271   2◇

272   2◇   These 2◇ rebids accomplish two things: they give you a chance to play in diamonds and imply extra strength. If the auction starts: 1♡-1♠, 2◇-2NT, 3♡, opener suggests six hearts and four diamonds with at least 15 high-card points.

273   3◇   Forcing. Blackwood is a practical second choice.

274   4♡

275   3◇

276   3◇

277   4◇   6♡ is a good spot if responder has xx, Q10xx, Kxx, AJxx. He will cuebid 5♣ with that but sign off in 4♡ with a hand like xx, QJxx, xxx, AKxx.

278   2◇

279   2♡

280   1NT   Not so bad with a singleton spade *honor*. If you aren't willing to do this, you should open 1◇.

281   Pass   A 2♣ rebid is acceptable, since partner surely has support.

282   Pass

283   3◇

284   3◇

285   Raise partner to the two level.

286   Pass

287   2NT

288   Pass

289   3NT

290   3NT

291   3NT   It looks awful, but with both majors stopped, you've got to try it.

II. More Rebids by Opener

6
AQ32
Q742
KJ65

If you open 1♣, what will you bid over a 1♠ response? _____ 292

Are you willing to open 1◊ and rebid 2♣? _____ 293

Should you open at all? _____ 294

Q
QJ83
KQ93
A1094

Are you willing to rebid 1NT over a 1♠ response to 1♣ or 1◊? _____ 295

If you *aren't*, what should you open? _____ 296

If you *are*, what should you open? _____ 297

J4
AK63
AJ853
K8

If you open 1◊, what will you bid over a 1♠ response? _____ 298

Can you rebid 2♡ over a 2♣ response without overstating your strength?
_____ 299

Should you consider opening 1♡? _____ 300

Should you consider opening 1NT? _____ 301

KJ53
Q
AJ83
K1054

What's the only response that could affect your choice of opening bids?

_____ 302

If you are willing to pass this response, what should your opening bid be?

_____ 303

J9542
5
AKJ104
A8

If you open 1♠, can you bid 3◇ over a 2♡ response? _____ 304

If the bidding starts: 1♠-2♡, 2♠-2NT, is it safe for you to bid 3◇ next?

_____ 305

Should you consider opening 1◇? _____ 306

If the bidding starts: 1◇-1♡, 1♠-1NT, 2♣ or 2♡, can you describe your hand with a 2♠ rebid? _____ 307

AJ1053
QJ8654
K5
—

Can you rebid 2♠ if partner responds 2♣ or 2◇ to 1♡? _____ 308

Should you prefer to misdescribe your suit length or strength? _____ 309

Should you consider opening 1♠, preparing a 2♡ rebid? _____ 310

292 1NT, but it's a poor bid with a singleton spade and lack of playing tricks.

293 We wouldn't be. The flaws: You suggest a two-suited hand; you increase the level of the contract; you fail to limit your hand.

294 No.

295 Yes. Your singleton spade is an honor, and you have good intermediates.

296 1◇, planning to rebid 2♣. But the flaws remain.

297 1♣

298 2◇ or 2♡, both unattractive.

299 In 1990, a "reverse" generally doesn't apply after a 2/1 response.

300 Yes, but the auction may not be comfortable. Responder may raise to 2♡, or the bidding may start: 1♡-1♠, 2◇-2♡.

301 This would be the choice of most experts.

302 1NT

303 1♣

304 No.

305 No. You would suggest six spades and four diamonds. Responder might take a spade preference on two low spades.

306 Yes.

307 Yes.

308 Yes, but beware. If opener reverses, responder might go overboard.

309 We'd rather tell a white lie about suit length.

310 Yes.

To Describe a Hand — Responder's Problems

Plan how you would conduct the auction as responder on the following hands.

K6
82
A742
A9652

Opener bids 1♠. You'll respond 2♣, and if opener rebids . . .

2◇, you'll call   _____   311

2♡, you'll call   _____   312

2♠, you'll call   _____   313

2NT, you'll call   _____   314

3♣, you'll call   _____   315

3♡, you'll call   _____   316

3♠, you'll call   _____   317

4♣, you'll call   _____   318

AJ83
Q10763
Q4
82

Opener bids 1◊. You'll respond 1♡, and if opener rebids . . .

1♠, you'll call	_____	319
1NT, you'll call	_____	320
2♣, you'll call	_____	321
2◊, you'll call	_____	322
2♡, you'll call	_____	323
2♠, you'll call	_____	324
2NT, you'll call	_____	325
3♣, you'll call	_____	326
3◊, you'll call	_____	327
3♡, you'll call	_____	328
4♡, you'll call	_____	329

AKJ2
QJ5
853
K104

Opener bids 1♣. You'll respond 1♠, and if opener rebids . . .

1NT, you'll call   _____ 330

2♣, you'll call   _____ 331

2◇, you'll call   _____ 332

2♡, you'll call   _____ 333

2♠, you'll call   _____ 334

2NT, you'll call   _____ 335

3♣, you'll call   _____ 336

3♠, you'll call   _____ 337

4♠, you'll call   _____ 338

AK73
J1064
A4
J32

Opener bids 1♣. You'll respond 1♡, and if opener rebids . . .

1♠, you'll call _____ 339

1NT, you'll call _____ 340

2♣, you'll call _____ 341

2♡, you'll call _____ 342

2NT, you'll call _____ 343

3♣, you'll call _____ 344

3♡, you'll call _____ 345

4♡, you'll call _____ 346

AQ73
Q942
86
K92

Opener bids 1◇. You'll respond 1♡, and if opener rebids . . .

1♠, you'll call   _____   347

1NT, you'll call   _____   348

2♣, you'll call   _____   349

2◇, you'll call   _____   350

2♡, you'll call   _____   351

2♠, you'll call   _____   352

2NT, you'll call   _____   353

3♣, you'll call   _____   354

3◇, you'll call   _____   355

3♡, you'll call   _____   356

AJ9
9
Q108542
653

Opener bids 1♡. You'll respond 1NT, and if opener rebids . . .

2♣, you'll call _____ 357

2♢, you'll call _____ 358

2♡, you'll call _____ 359

2♠, you'll call _____ 360

2NT, you'll call _____ 361

3♣, you'll call _____ 362

3♢, you'll call _____ 363

3♡, you'll call _____ 364

3NT, you'll call _____ 365

Q73
43
AQ742
AK8

Opener bids 1♠. You'll respond 2◊, and if opener rebids . . .

2♡, you'll call	_____	366
2♠, you'll call	_____	367
2NT, you'll call	_____	368
3♣, you'll call	_____	369
3◊, you'll call	_____	370

311   3◇

312   2NT   2♠ is not an error, but 2NT offers more encouragement.

313   3♠   Not strong enough to bid 3◇, committing the hand to game.

314   3NT   Pass could be the winner if opener's 2NT shows no extras.

315   3◇   3♣ is forcing as most pairs play. You must try for game, since opener may be strong.

316   3♠   Opener promises a big major two-suiter; K-6 is good support. You will cuebid next.

317   4◇   Since your cards are great for slam in spades, you can afford one slam try under the game level. Still, we wouldn't criticize severely a cautious 4♠ bid.

318   4◇   A grand slam isn't out of the question. Plan to bid 4♠ over opener's 4♡.

319   2♠   A jump to 3♠, if invitational, is possible; the ◇Q is upgraded.

320   Pass   A rebid of 2♡ could work, but may backfire if partner is short.

321   2◇   Not enough to bid 2NT. If opener tries again with 2♡ or 2NT, you will bid game.

322   Pass   Very close. Your ◇Q is gold and 3NT may be cold. However, if you raise, opener will bid game on many hands that offer no play.

323   3♡   Game try. The heart fit has improved the hand.

324   4♠   Good support.

325   3♠   Looking for the best game.

326   3◇   Most flexible bid for now. There may be a slam if opener can support hearts. Over 3♡, you'll bid 3♠. If opener has no heart support, he can bid 3♠, the fourth suit, asking for notrump.

327 3♠ Best game is still uncertain. Plan to pass 3NT or 4♡, or raise 4◊ to 5◊.

328 4♡

329 4♠ Worth one slam try, but you'll sign off in 5♡ over 5♣/5◊.

330 3NT

331 2♡ Hoping to hear 2NT. If opener prefers spades, you can try 4♠ on the 4-3 fit. If he rebids 3♣, raise to 4♣. If he raises hearts (ulp!), bid 4♣.

332 2NT Letting opener, who promises another bid, clarify. Since your diamond holding is poor, you may settle for 3NT.

333 3♣ Same idea, but the heart fit makes slam chances better. For example, if opener continues with 3♠, you can hardly stay out of 6♣ with all your cards working. A jump to 4♣ is reasonable.

334 3♡ Gives partner the chance to bid 3NT. Otherwise it's back to 4♠.

335 4NT Close to 6NT, but it usually pays to give partner some leeway.

336 4♣ Forcing. Too much slam potential to speculate with 3NT or try a devious 3♡.

337 4♣ Opener's hand is unbalanced, so you're barely worth a slam try.

338 4NT Blackwood, just in case you are off two aces.

339 3♠ If you play it forcing; otherwise, you must bid game.

340 3NT

341 3NT Second choice: 2♠. However, complications may set in if you mess around, and making the value bid doesn't rule out a slam.

342 2♠ With poor hearts, give yourself a chance to play 3NT.

343   4NT   A quantitative slam try.

344   4♣   Forcing. You will surely bid slam, maybe a grand. If partner can bid 4◇ or 4♡, you'll bid 4♠, hoping he will Blackwood.

345   3♠   Plan to bid 4◇ over 4♣. Even with the poor trumps, the hand is worth two slam tries.

346   6♡

347   3♠

348   2NT

349   2NT

350   2NT

351   2NT

352   4♠   The alternative, 3♠, will endplay you if partner tries for slam. A direct jump to game, *when a lower bid in the same suit is forcing,* shows slam interest with strong trumps and nothing to cuebid.

353   3NT

354   3NT   Slightly conservative, but you have no fit.

355   3NT

356   4♡

357   2◇

358   2♠   You show a big diamond fit and values in spades. Pass if opener signs off in 2NT or 3NT or returns to 3◇. Convert 3♡ to 4◇, and 3♣ to 3◇. However, if opener rebids 3♠, you can jump to 5◇, with no wasted values in clubs.

359   Pass

360   3◇   A raise to 3♠ is possible since you failed to respond 1♠ originally.

361   3◇   Sign off.

362   3◇

363   3♠   Advance cuebid.

364   Pass   Second choice: 4◇, which might hit the nail on the head if partner has three cards in diamonds and raises, but will fail when partner rebids 4♡ and goes down.

365   Pass

366   3♠   If opener bids 4♠, you'll try for slam with a 5♣ cuebid.

367   3♣   If opener rebids 3◇ or 3♡, bid 3♠. Convert 3NT or 4♣ to 4♠. If opener rebids 3♠, bid 5♠ to demand slam if he has a heart control.

368   3♠   Forcing.

369   3♠   The only question is whether you will bid a grand slam or stop at six. Set the trump suit now, planning to use the Grand Slam Force or Key Card Blackwood, if available, later.

370   3♠   Awkward. It's tempting to bid 4♣, starting the slam search. But opener could be minimum, and you might want to play in spades, especially at matchpoint scoring. If opener bids 4♠, try for slam with 5♣, not 5♠, which would get you to slam *any time* opener has a heart control. Opener could have AKJxx, Kxx, Jxxx, Q. If opener does anything encouraging over 3♠, bid at least a small slam.

QUICK QUIZ

Hats

Match the following noted bridge personalities with their current or former occupations away from the bridge table.

371	Alfred Sheinwold	*chairman of pharmaceuticals company*
372	Mike Lawrence	*gold trader in Switzerland*
373	Benito Garozzo	*administrative judge*
374	Chip Martel	*OSS cryptanalyst*
375	James Cayne	*insurance agent*
376	Beth Palmer	*physician*
377	Kathie Wei	*attorney*
378	Hugh Ross	*banker*
379	John Fisher	*nurse*
380	Norman Kay	*accountant*
381	Bob Hamman	*gift shop owner*
382	Zia Mahmood	*systems analyst*
383	Richard Walsh	*president of Bear Stearns*
384	Marshall Miles	*author of book on "scrabble"*
385	Pietro Forquet	*professor of computer science*
386	George Rosenkranz	*Merrill-Lynch investment executive*

371   Alfred Sheinwold-OSS cryptanalyst during WWII

372   Mike Lawrence-author of "scrabble" book

373   Benito Garozzo-gift shop owner

374   Chip Martel-professor of computer science

375   James Cayne-president of Bear Stearns

376   Beth Palmer-administrative judge

377   Kathie Wei-nurse

378   Hugh Ross-systems analyst

379   John Fisher-physician

380   Norman Kay-investment executive

381   Bob Hamman-insurance agent

382   Zia Mahmood-accountant

383   Richard Walsh-gold trader in Switzerland

384   Marshall Miles-attorney

385   Pietro Forquet-banker

386   George Rosenkranz-chairman of pharmaceuticals company

Bridge Movies — 1

Here are three hands for you to bid and play in the style of *Bridge World* magazine's "Bridge Movies." Use a piece of paper to cover the page, uncovering it as you read. When you come to a question (*italics*), decide on your answer before reading further.

I.

As South, playing in the first final session of the Life Master Pairs, you hold:

> 3
> 72
> AQ8653
> AQ96

Neither side is vulnerable. After a pass on your right, you open 1◇, partner responds 1♠. The opponents remain silent. *What is your rebid?* _____ 387

387   2◇, to suggest a minimum with long diamonds. Although a 2♣ rebid wouldn't deny a minimum, it wouldn't suggest one either — that could cause trouble down the road.

Partner next bids 2♡. *What do you say?* _____ 388

388   3♣, showing a minimum with (probably) six diamonds and four clubs. A notrump bid would be premature; if notrump is the spot, partner probably should be declarer. True, you might bid 3♣ on a hand like this: xx, Kx, AQ10xxx, Axx, trying to maneuver partner into being declarer at notrump. But he can't assume that you don't have clubs merely because you introduced the dreaded fourth suit.

Partner jumps to 4◇. *Is that forcing?* _____ 389

389   Yes. With an invitational hand partner would either raise 2◇ to 3◇ or bid 3◇ over 3♣.

Should you cuebid 5♣ now? _____ 390

390   Yes, since your hand is limited. Partner's hand is unlimited, and he may
       be interested in slam. Since he seems to be short in clubs, he may be
       happy to hear about your ace.

       Over 5♣ partner jumps to 6◊, and all pass. West leads the ♡J.

                                AJ865
                                A4
                                J9742
                                4

                                3
                                72
                                AQ8653
                                AQ96

                    NORTH   SOUTH
                    —   1◊
                    1♠   2◊
                    2♡   3♣
                    4◊   5♣
                    6◊

What do you think of partner's bidding? _____ 391

391   It was optimistic, with only 10 points in high cards. (Some players would
       have jumped to 4◊ over 2◊, forcing — that bid would have implied
       good distribution since it aimed at an 11-trick contract. Partner
       preferred a sequence that sounded slightly stronger and implied club
       shortness.) Partner's jump to 6◊ on J-x-x-x-x was aggressive.

Do you take the ♡A? What is your general plan? _____

_____ 392

392   Win the first trick. If you can pick up the trumps, the slam is in the
       bag. If not, you can try to do something about your heart loser.

On the ♡A East signals with the 9. You lead the ◇J to the ace — you have no reason to go against percentage — and West's king falls. You are safe for 12 tricks. *What would you have done if East had discarded on the first trump play?* 393

393   You would have crossed to the ♠A and taken the club finesse. To set up the spades, you would need to find West with exactly four, which is less than a 30% chance. (If West had three spades, he could overruff you on the fourth spade and cash a heart.) Also, the chance that East has long clubs, including the king, increases if he is short in diamonds.

What if East had started with K10 of trumps? _____394

394   If East showed up with the ◇K10, you would play West for the ♣K, and try to set up spades. You could ruff three spades in your hand while ruffing three clubs in dummy and finally lead the fifth spade for a discard of your heart.

When the ◇K drops, how do you play for an overtrick? _____ 395

395   It would be crazy to finesse the ♣Q to get a heart discard, jeopardizing your good result. Try to set up the spades.

You lead a spade to the ace and ruff a spade, cash the ♣A and ruff a club, East following with the 10. On the next spade East plays the 9, you ruff and West discards a heart. So much for the spades. *Now what?* _____ 396

396   You can still make seven if East has a stiff club honor left. The principle of restricted choice suggests that East has the ♣K — if he started with J-10-x, he could have played either the jack or the 10 on the second round; if he had K-10-x, he would have had no choice.

Should you rely on that? _____ 397

397   No. East is a passed hand and has shown ♠KQ9xx. He has the ♡Q and probably has the ♡K, because of West's failure to overcall one heart. Therefore East cannot hold the ♣K. Lead the ♣Q and try to pin the jack.

The full deal (see top of next page):

```
                        AJ865
                        A4
                        J9742
                        4
        104                            KQ972
        J10863                         KQ95
        K                              10
        K8532                          J107
                        3
                        72
                        AQ8653
                        AQ96
```

II.

As South, playing in the first match of a sectional Swiss teams event, you pick up:

```
                        753
                        AKJ94
                        A105
                        A4
```

Both sides are vulnerable. *What is your opening bid?* _____ 398

398   1NT. This descriptive opening avoids the rebid problems that arise after a 1♡ opening. You may land in notrump when hearts is better, but it's less likely to matter at IMPs.

If you had only two spades, you would be reluctant to open 1NT. Partner might transfer to spades with five spades and three hearts, marooning you in the wrong spot.

Partner raises to 2NT. *What do you say?* _____ 399

399   Bid 3♡. Partner's failure to use Stayman increases the chance he has a doubleton spade, in which case 4♡ could easily play better than 3NT.

Partner rebids 3NT, all pass and West leads the ♠2.

> KQ6
> 52
> 9832
> K753
>
>
> 753
> AKJ94
> A105
> A4

NORTH	SOUTH
--	1NT
2NT	3♡
3NT	

Dummy's ♠K holds the first trick, and you try a heart to the jack, losing to West's queen. West cashes the ♠A and continues a spade to the queen, East following. *What do you do next?* _____ 400

400   Lead a diamond to the 10. Since you can afford to lose two more tricks, delay the crucial heart play for a while.

West wins the ◇Q and cashes the 13th spade. You and dummy throw diamonds, East discards the ♣10. A low-club shift goes to East's queen and your ace. When you cash your ◇A, both opponents follow low. When you lead a club to the king, East plays the 9.
   You can't postpone leading a second heart any longer. *What do you do?*
_____ 401

401   Lead a heart to the 9. Spades are known to be 4-3, and clubs were probably 4-3 also, judging from the defenders' plays (with QJ109, East would have first thrown the queen). As for diamonds, West cleared the spades instead of leading a second low spade to keep communication — he indicates a sure entry, which can only be the ◇K. But with K-Q-J-x or K-Q-x-x, West might have led a diamond instead of a spade, so diamonds are probably 3-3. Hearts, therefore, should be 2-4. The full deal (see top of next page):

```
                    KQ6
                    52
                    9832
                    K753
      A1042                        J98
      Q7                           10863
      KQ4                          J76
      J862                         Q109
                    753
                    AKJ94
                    A105
                    A4
```

Other clues were available. For example, if East had three low hearts, he might have thrown a heart instead of a club from Q-10-9. With four diamonds, East surely would have pitched a diamond.

III.

As South, playing in a prize-money individual (scored by IMPs), you find yourself facing a player with a gleam in his eye. You have never seen him before. You hold:

```
                    A93
                    Q43
                    K2
                    KJ943
```

You open 1♣, and partner responds 1♡. The opponents stay out. *What is your rebid?* _____ 402

402   1NT. Nothing is wrong with raising a major-suit response on three-card support — *if* partner is aware that you will do this. Playing with a new and scary partner, your tendency should be to make bids that will not lead to a disaster. 1NT is surely safe.

Over 1NT, partner bids 2◊. You are not sure if he means this as forcing or not, but in either case you have an easy heart preference. *However, should it be 2♡ or 3♡?* _____ 403

403   2♡. Granted you are worth a jump now, having denied a raise on the first round. But the mad look in partner's eye indicates caution.

Partner next bids 3♣. For what it's worth, the tournament conventions stated that all second-round jumps are forcing. Does this mean that he intended his sequence as not forcing? Maybe, but the point is moot since you have enough to accept an invitation. *What call should you make?* _____ 404

404   3♠. This is your most flexible action for now. You show something good in spades, and give him a chance to clarify his heart length. Partner, who rates to have a three-suiter short in spades, can try clubs or hearts, and then you'll know where to place the contract.

Partner bids 3NT. *What do you do?* _____ 405

405   Pass. You bid 3♠ to let partner make the final decision. You hope he has a doubleton spade and only four hearts. In either case, you are happy to be declarer when facing a man with a gleam in his eye. The contract becomes 3NT. West leads the ♠6.

Q5
AK92
AQ104
652

A93
Q43
K2
KJ943

NORTH	SOUTH
--	1♣
1♡	1NT
2◇	2♡
3♣	3♠
3NT	pass

What do you think of partner's bidding? _____ 406

406   He might have started with 1◊ and should have bid 3NT over 1NT.

What do you play from dummy at trick one? _____ 407

407   The queen is twice as good a play as the 5.

The ♠Q holds, East encouraging with the 8. You can count eight top tricks with many chances for one more. *What do you do at trick two?* _____ 408

408   The red suits can wait. We suggest leading a club to the *king*. If West has the ace (without the queen), he may duck to preserve an entry.

Alas, West takes your ♣K with the ace and returns the ♠4 to East's jack. You hold up your ace and win the third spade. Dummy discards a club. *What now?* _____ 409

409   Cash the top diamonds and throw a club. Both defenders follow low; the jack is still out. *How do you continue?* _____ 410

410   Try the hearts. You cash the ace and queen, and East plays the jack on the second round. When you lead a third heart, West follows low. *Do you finesse the 9?* _____ 411

411   Suppose you go up with the ♡K, and East discards. That would mean West started with 5-4-3-1 pattern, and leading a second club would be safe. East could win and cash the ◊J, but he would have to give you the ♣J in the end. So it can't be right to finesse the ♡9.

The full deal:

	Q5	
	AK92	
	AQ104	
	652	
K10764		J82
875		J106
963		J875
AQ		1087
	A93	
	Q43	
	K2	
	KJ943	

Partnership Perspectives

Intangibles such as mutual respect, morale and will to win determine a pair's success or failure as much as technical skills and bidding system. Take the following "quiz" to see how you measure up in the partnership department.

412　The only excuse for "discussing" a disastrous result right at the table is:

(A)　to properly humble partner.
(B)　to give the opponents' morale a boost.
(C)　to make sure everyone understands that the disaster wasn't your fault.
(D)　to prevent a recurrence of the disaster in the same session.

413　Partner errs on defense, letting a beatable contract make. You quickly point out what he should have done. A probable result is partner will:

(A)　be eternally grateful to you.
(B)　be inspired by your words and play double dummy for the rest of the session.
(C)　pick up the duplicate board and bonk you in the nose.
(D)　dwell on his error and have difficulty concentrating on the remaining boards.

414　A convention is:

(A)　something American Legion members attend.
(B)　something signed in Geneva to govern the treatment of prisoners of war.
(C)　a call such as a limit raise or an inverted minor-suit raise.
(D)　a call such as Stayman that acts like a coded message.

415　An appropriate topic for partnership discussion is:

(A)　partner's shortcomings in dummy play.
(B)　partner's silly lapses in concentration.
(C)　what books on defensive play partner should read.
(D)　cuebidding philosophy in slam auctions.

416   The best procedure for a constructive review of the session is:

(A) partner tells you how well you bid and played.
(B) you criticize his bidding and play; he gratefully acknowledges your help.
(C) you and partner criticize each other's bidding and play.
(D) you and partner criticize each other *and yourselves.*

417   Among the possible drawbacks to a splinter response is:

(A) an opponent may double to suggest a safe opening lead.
(B) an opponent may double to suggest a good sacrifice.
(C) ambiguity in handling voids, singleton aces and singleton kings.
(D) all of the above.

418   First-time partnerships often do well because:

(A) the players display their most supportive behavior.
(B) the players employ a relatively uncomplicated system.
(C) the players take care to avoid ambiguous bids and defensive plays.
(D) all of the above.

419   Which question should you *not* ask yourself before adding a new convention to your system?

(A) Is the convention easy to remember?
(B) How often does the chance to use it occur?
(C) Does it replace a natural bid that is useful?
(D) Do Marty Bergen-Larry Cohen play it?

420   In a competitive auction, your partner doubles the opponents in 4♠ and they wrap up +790. Your best move is to:

(A) retreat into a sulky silence.
(B) announce that you certainly had your bids.
(C) ask the opponents what they would have done with partner's hand.
(D) say "Tough luck, partner" and go on to the next board.

421   Most players who criticize their partner do so because:

(A) they can't control their righteous indignation at seeing bridge played imperfectly.
(B) they believe in the "do-unto-partner-before-he-can-do-unto-you" approach.
(C) they're naturally assertive.
(D) they're insecure; their egos are threatened because their partner erred.

422   The ideal partnership consists of:

(A) two players who don't like each other.
(B) two players with strong emotional ties.
(C) two players, each of whom thinks the other is a hopeless player.
(D) two players who cultivate mutual respect and detachment.

423   You are eager to play Mushroom, that neat convention you heard about last weekend. You sit down before the game and find out that partner isn't familiar with Mushroom. You:

(A) offer to give him a quick summary before the game starts.
(B) teach it to him between boards.
(C) deride his lack of knowledge of modern conventions.
(D) wait until time is available for a thorough discussion of Mushroom.

424   If you're the stronger player in a partnership, you should always try to:

(A) be declarer even if the contract isn't best.
(B) mastermind the bidding so your side gets to the best spot.
(C) make certain your partner knows who is carrying whom.
(D) bid and play normally, maintaining your own good habits while giving partner practice and confidence.

425 If you're the weaker player in a partnership, you should:

(A) apologize after every bad board.
(B) compliment your partner's play on every hand.
(C) try to steer the declaring to partner's side.
(D) do none of the above.

426   Dlr: East   8
      Vul: E-W   87
                         J95
                         KJ106532
         107532   KQ964
         Q10943   AKJ2
         83   A2
         4   Q8
                         AJ
                         65
                         KQ10764
                         A97

WEST	NORTH	EAST	SOUTH
--	--	1♠	2◊
4♠	5◊	Dbl	All Pass

Since a diamond lead would beat 5♠, East's double of 5◊ was correct. West led his singleton club to the jack, queen and ace. Declarer led a diamond to East's ace. After ruffing the club return, however, West tried for the setting trick in spades. South produced the ♠A and claimed his contract.

East hotly criticized partner's spade return, contending that he, East, was a lock to hold the ♡A for his double of 5◊. The most likely reason for this diatribe was that:

(A) East disliked South and was upset at seeing him score up +550.
(B) East had his faults, but he was certain that being wrong wasn't one of them.
(C) East had a substantial bet on the outcome of the match.
(D) East realized he should have laid down the ♡K before returning a club.

427 Dlr: North   KJ53
     Vul: None   K6
                         AQ6
                         J853

     742   86
     QJ1075   A943
     J73   109854
     K4   AQ

                         AQ109
                         82
                         K2
                         109762

WEST	NORTH	EAST	SOUTH
--	1♣	Pass	1♠
Pass	2♠	Pass	3♣
Pass	4♠	All Pass	

West leads the ♡Q, covered by the king and ace. East returns a heart to the 10, and West shifts to a diamond, won by dummy's ace. Declarer draws trumps, then leads a club from hand. West, not sure what is going on in the minors, finally puts up the ♣K. At this point, East can hasten the demise of the partnership by:

(A) informing everybody that E-W are cold for 4♡.
(B) overtaking with the ♣A and giving West a disgusted look.
(C) laughing uproariously at West's play.
(D) any of the above, but especially (B).

428   Dlr: South
      Vul: E-W

```
                        A653
                        83
                        J53
                        J642
        942                          J107
        KJ952                        Q104
        A7                           Q1096
        753                          Q108
                        KQ8
                        A76
                        K842
                        AK9
```

WEST	NORTH	EAST	SOUTH
--	--	--	1◊
Pass	1♠	Pass	2NT
All Pass			

West leads a low heart, and declarer holds off the ace until the third round. He cashes the ♣AK, then runs four rounds of spades. East discards a diamond, West throws a club. Now declarer leads a diamond . . . 10, king, ace.

True or false? At this point West should cash his two good hearts.

429   If you switch from Standard to a forcing club system, don't be surprised if you have:

(A)   more accuracy in game and slam auctions, less accuracy in partscore auctions.
(B)   less accuracy when opener has a minimum opening with long clubs.
(C)   more misunderstandings because many sequences are suddenly undefined.
(D)   all of the above.

430   As South, both vulnerable at IMPs, you hold:

KJ76
AQ6
65
A763

WEST	NORTH	EAST	SOUTH
—	—	—	1♣
Pass	1♠	Pass	2♠
Pass	3◊	Pass	?

You should:

(A) bid 3♠.
(B) bid 3NT.
(C) bid 3♡.
(D) bid 4♠.

431   Major championships are most often decided when:

(A) someone finds a devastating opening lead on the last board.
(B) someone manages to reach a cold 19-point grand slam on the last round.
(C) someone makes 7♠ on a triple squeeze on the next-to-last board.
(D) someone earns themselves a zero by having a silly bidding misunderstanding on board 17.

432   True or false? Two good players using simple bidding and carding methods will be more effective than two poor players armed with the latest in modern gadgets.

433   The most vital consideration about a bidding system is:

(A) to play a lot of conventions.
(B) to play the conventions the professionals play.
(C) to play only conventions that have been written up in someone's book.
(D) to have a good understanding of the conventions you do play.

434   True or false? A good partnership, in reviewing a session, should take note of their good boards as well as their bad ones.

435   Among the drawbacks to the Flannery convention are:

(A) opener cannot show the quality of his major suits.
(B) responder alone bears the burden of placing the contract.
(C) a weak two-bid in diamonds is unavailable.
(D) all of the above.

436   Your most effective overcalling style is likely to be:

(A) "shows 13 points or more."
(B) "shows 13 cards or more."
(C) "promises a good suit but no makes no other guarantees."
(D) "a consistent style, which reflects your partnership's philosophy."

437   True or false? For maximum efficiency, an expert partnership should expect to spend *hundreds* of hours discussing their methods.

438   As South, both vulnerable at IMPs, you hold:

--
A96
KJ10653
AQ62

WEST	NORTH	EAST	SOUTH
--	--	--	1◇
3♠	Dbl (penalty)	Pass	?

You should:

(A) bid 4◇.
(B) bid 4♣.
(C) bid 3NT.
(D) pass.

439   As South, both vulnerable at IMPs, you hold:

> J1065
> 65
> AQ96
> KJ3

WEST	NORTH	EAST	SOUTH
1♡	Pass	2♡	Pass
Pass	2♠	3♡	?

You should:

(A) bid 4♠.
(B) bid 3♠.
(C) double.
(D) pass.

440   Your partner thinks the Sunflower convention is worth a try; you think it has serious flaws. Your best move is to:

(A) dissolve the partnership.
(B) insist on your own point of view.
(C) flip a coin.
(D) offer to give Sunflower a trial before making a final decision.

441   Your partner opens 1♡. Which hand is suitable for a limit raise?

(A) AQJ5, QJ65, 654, 54
(B) A76, Q106, A765, J43
(C) 87, KJ5, AKJ65, 543
(D) 86, KJ65, A8653, 53

442   Negative doubles are justly popular because:

(A) they are simple and effective.
(B) you get to use them often.
(C) you can use them and still penalize an opposing overcall.
(D) all of the above.

443   When you adopt negative doubles, you must decide:

(A) whether opening bidder *must* reopen after an overcall is followed by two passes.
(B) whether you will permit "one-suit" negative doubles.
(C) whether opener promises extra values in the bidding sequence: 1♣-1♠-Dbl-Pass, 2◊.
(D) all of the above.

444   Driving to a sectional tournament, you and partner decide to add a new convention to your arsenal. The chances that you'll get to use the convention that weekend are about:

(A) 85%.
(B) 55%.
(C) 35%.
(D) 15%.

445   The best time for partnership discussion is:

(A) between hands.
(B) between sessions.
(C) over a large stiff drink in the bar after the game.
(D) in a relaxed, objective atmosphere after you get home from the tournament.

446   Any partnership's most important guideline should be:

(A) "gold points at all costs."
(B) the Rule of Eleven.
(C) "he who has the gold makes the rules."
(D) the Golden Rule.

412   D

413   D

414   D   Limit raises and inverted minor-suit raises are examples of *treatments*.

415   D

416   D

417   D

418   D

419   D

420   D   (C), incidentally, is the worst. *Never* appeal to the opponents.

421   D

422   D

423   D

424   D

425   D

426   D

427   D

428   False. West can cash one heart, but then he should lead a diamond to let partner claim. West knows that East must have the minor-suit queens left. If West cashes his last heart, East must spend valuable mental energy deciding which queen to keep.

429   D

430   D   Avoid 3♡ unless you like to torture partner with devious bids when a straightforward bid is available.

431   D

432   True

433   D

434   True

435   D

436   D

437   True

438   D

439   D   Partner bid your cards when he balanced. Don't punish him for his enterprise. Perhaps you can go plus against 3♡.

440   D

441   D   (A) has concentrated side-suit values and should bid spades before raising hearts. (B) has only three trumps and is suitable for a forcing 1NT or 2◇ response. (C) has only three trumps and is too strong for a limit raise.

442   D

443   D

444   D

445   D   (C) has also been known to work.

446   D

Convention Jungle

This is a two-part puzzle. First, solve the clues below to get the names of 30 modern conventions and treatments. Then find the names in the giant letter maze at the conclusion of this quiz. Par time: two hours.

447   It's a pain if you have
       one of these in your hand.   _ _ _ _ _ _ _ _

448   A city in Michigan, or a
       quartz-like mineral.   _ _ _ _ _

449   Convention for bidding over
       a notrump opening was devised   _ _ _ _ _ _
       by Bernard Zeller.

450   Chicken dish is named after
       this conventional 2◊ opening   _ _ _ _ _ _ _ _
       that shows the majors.

451   Surprisingly, not all bridge
       writers play these defensive   _ _ _ _ _ _ _ _ _ _
       carding methods.
                                           _ _ _ _ _

452   Originator allegedly devised
       this convention to cope with
       Eric Murray's frequent light   _ _ _ _ _
       opening bids.

453   Ace-asking convention no doubt
       favored by noted baby food maker.   _ _ _ _ _ _

454   What Jim Henson might have
       used when he wanted to find   _ _ _ _ _ _
       a 4-4 major-suit fit.
                                           _ _ _ _ _ _ _

455   2◊ opening has many possible   _ _ _ _ _
meanings in this British
convention; hence its name.

456   Translated from the German,   _ _ _ _ _ _ _ _ _
the name of this versatile
convention means "life's
reward."

457   Conventional method used after   _ _ _ _ _
opener's jump rebid to 2NT
was devised by the only player   _ _ _ _ _ _ _
to win four different WBF
world championship events.

458   Double of preempt is for penalty   _ _ _ _ _ _ _ _
in this out-of-favor convention.

459   Culbertson said they were his   _ _ _ _ _ _
greatest technical achievement
and biggest P.R. failure.   _ _ _ _

460   The K-S cornerstone   _ _ _ _ _

     _ _ _ _ _ _ _

461   Easley the best-known convention   _ _ _ _ _ _ _ _ _
of all.

462   Austrian-born conductor of San   _ _ _ _ _ _
Diego Opera invented conven-
tional method that contains the
germ of modern relay systems.

463   Knowledgable bridge teachers   _ _ _ _ _
tell their students to call
it a "prepared opening bid."   _ _ _ _

464   Longtime Goren associate developed this scheme for rebidding after an opening weak two-bid.

           _ _ _ _ _

465   Rodney Dangerfield might be right at home using this psychic overcall.

           _ _ _ _ _

           _ _ _ _ _ _ _

466   Name of cuebid you're using if you bid 2♡ over 1♡ to show spades and clubs.

           _ _ _ _ _ _ _ _

467   Convention named for state that hosted Spring NABC in '78, '84 and '90.

           _ _ _ _ _

468   Informal name for this treatment is "1-2-3-Stop."

           _ _ _ _ _ _ _ _ _

           _ _ _ _ _ _ _

469   In this "appetizing" bidding style, you bid your shorter suit first.

           _ _ _ _ _ _

470   A petite flower lends it name to this conventional double that shows length in the unbid suit plus a tolerance for partner's suit.

           _ _ _ _ _ _ _ _

471   Ely Culbertson espoused the strong first cousin of this modern competitive bid.

           _ _ _ _   _ _ _ _

           _ _ _ _ _ _ _

472   Method to show a minor two-suiter can backfire if an opponent uses knowledge of your distribution in playing the dummy.

   _ _ _ _ _ _ _

   _ _ _ _ _ _ _

473   California player's device lets 1NT opener be declarer in a 3-5 major-suit fit.

   _ _ _ _ _ _

474   Wei's way to plug a hole in Precision: how to respond with a strong 4-4-4-1 hand.

   _ _ _ _ _ _ _ _

   _ _ _ _ _ _ _

475   In the auction — 1♠-3♠, 4NT-5♡, 6♣-7♠ — the 6♣ bid is this convention.

   _ _ _ _ _ _ _

   _ _ _ _ _

476   Originally part of K-S, it wins when you reach game on a good fit, but loses when the opponents get help in the defense or find a good save.

   _ _ _ _ _ _ _ _ _

   _ _ _ _ _ _ _

The Jungle

Find the 30 conventions inside this maze.
(Draw a circle around each one.)

```
S P L I N G E R C O D T G P F A S G S B B S A X E T S H W R D
B R O N E Z O R B R O E R U T I E D L A C K W O O D H U E O P
L A F R O L O C U G M X A R N R S A A S K I B I B J O N A F M
N E B R E G F U U S U A N T B N C H M E G T S W O I R U K M A
L E B E N S R S H O L R B O A K E U B R L N R U E G T S J A R
R C O C O M I C N O T R U M P U L L A E A T R O E A W U U A T
L I B R E G I F E D I E L K A L A N O P I N S R H E L A M L O
H A C O B S R I R I I Z C A I C D S D M A N B I A S U L M S N
L E B F I S H S O O R O T E K S H R E L S E L K L I B N E D K
N O P M U R T H M W R R W L O A E S I A R N D N A M O R N A
A K R A X E T B S K U B O A R G N E P A N O W E A R N T S A E
O F L L N A M O R C R O H T G W E A K J T E X I S E S R I R W
H L H S S A T R E A D M S I S N A P D R A G O N N R H U U G A
S A O D H E C N A L F I N L A H U N U K R A R E R E O M L O C
O N S N A M U L T B U L F I S L O M T A E W L A O V R P M U J
F N N A D F E L O T U L W A L N P R N S D I B G N I K S A X E
H N E R D N F R G M A L K A R A U R T F M O N G I T F F L O W
S E B G E R B O R N L A C N O M Y A T S T E P P U P S E X E T
I R E E B A H I N L G R O T P O T S U G U A U S U M X E T W A
F I L R D P S E L G E E K N U R T O N K N I W H G E A L S R G
I T R R P S R U R V I E N T L O I N A M Y A T S T E P P U P B
N E U A O Y M O O B E S A U S U H S U N U R E G E R R B G R K
G R N P G E R P R E E M F T I V E S R A T L U M A P A B O T A
Y A M O P A M A R T A R A F L E N N E E R Y L A I M I Z E H E
C I T S S U G O F A O T T E L I N S W A T R N I G R E K A E W
L E B E J A P R A L O N T N I O L F O O F N E B E L E T B E L
U N U K X E N C O M I C N O T W W O O M P L I A R R A B R E G
B R A Z O A R C O M I N T R E B R E L U S U A L N O T R U Y P
D E X E L B O O D E V I T A G E N E L B I S S O P M I G E R B
W G R A G R A N D S L A M F A R C E F R U R Y R E S R E G E R
```

447 Splinter	457 Wolff signoff	467 Texas
448 Flint	458 Fishbein	468 Preemptive reraise
449 Brozel	459 Asking bids	469 Canape
450 Flannery	460 Weak notrump	470 Snapdragon
451 Journalist leads	461 Blackwood	471 Weak jump overcall
452 Drury	462 Herbert	472 Unusual notrump
453 Gerber	463 Short club	473 Smolen
454 Puppet Stayman	464 Ogust	474 Impossible negative
455 Multi	465 Comic notrump	475 Grand slam force
456 Lebensohl	466 Colorful	476 Short suit game try

```
* * * * * G * * * * * * * F * S * * * * S A X E T * * * * *
* * * * E * * * * * * * * I * D * * * * * * * * * U * * *
* * * R * * * * * M * * * * S * A * * * * * * * * N * * *
* * B * * * * * * U * * * N * H * E * * * * * * * U * * *
* E * E * * * * * L * B * * E * B * L * * * * * * S * * *
R * * C O M I C N O T R U M P * * L * E * T * * * * W U * *
* * * R * * * * * I * L * * * A * O * I * S * * E * A * * *
* * * O * * * * * * C * * C * * * M * N * I A S * L * * *
* E * F * * * * * * * T * K * * * * S * * K L I * N * * *
* * P M * * * * * * * R W * * * * * * * N * * A * O * * *
* * * A * * * * * * * * O * * * * * * * O * * R N T * * *
* * L L N * * * * * * O H * * * * * * T * * * * E * R * * *
* * H S * A * * * * D * S * S N A P D R A G O N * R * U U * *
* * O D * * C * * * * * * * * H * * U * * * * * * E * M * O *
* * S N * * * * * * * * F * * L O M * * * * * * * V * P * * J
* * N A * F * * * * * L * * L * P R * S D I B G N I K S A * *
* * E R * * F * * * A * * A * * * * T * * * * * * T * * * *
* * B G * * * O * N * * C * * * * * * S * * * * * P * * * *
* * E * * * H * N * * R * * * * * * * U * * * * M * * T * * *
* * L * D * * E * G E * * * * * * * * * I * * * E * * S * *
* * * R * * R * R V I * * * L * * N A M Y A T S T E P P U P B
* * U * * Y * O B * S * U * * * * * * * * G * R * * G R *
* R * * * * P * * E * F * * * * * R * * * * A P * * O * *
Y * * * * * M * * * * R * F * * * * E * * * * M * Z * * *
* * * * * U * * F * O * T * L * * * * * T * * * * * E * * *
* * * * J * * * * L * * * * * O * * * * N * * L * T * * *
* * * K * * * * O * I * * * * * W * * * * * I * * * * R * *
* * A * * * C * * N * * * * * * * * * * * * L * * * * Y *
* E * * * * * * * E V I T A G E N E L B I S S O P M I * * * *
W * * * * * * * * * * * * * * * * * * * * * * * * S * * * *
```

Play 'em Safe, Play 'em Right

A good declarer considers the deal as a whole in planning his play. However, he must also know how to handle individual suit combinations. In the following situations, assume that there are no clues from the bidding or play and that plenty of entries to each hand are available. Some of the problems require true safety plays — correct play guarantees the required number of tricks. In others, the right play isn't guaranteed but does guard against a particular adverse distribution.

I. Play 'em Safe

477   AK93   You need to assure three tricks.

☐

J542

478   KJ43   You need three tricks.

☐

A52

479   AK8543   You need to assure five tricks.

☐

J62

480   A95   You need to assure five tricks.

☐

QJ6432

481   K93   You need four tricks.

□

AQ542

482   AKQ832   You need to assure five tricks.

□

104

483   AKQJ92   You need five tricks.

□

4

484   K62   You need three tricks.

□

Q10853

485   KQ86543   You need to assure five tricks.

□

102

486   AQ542   You need four tricks.

□

8763

487   5432   You need two tricks.

□

KQ76

488   A107632   You need to assure five tricks.

□

Q854

489   AJ2   You need to assure four tricks.

□

K9543

490   A10543   You need three tricks.

□

J62

491   AQ543   You need three tricks.

□

1062

492   A105   You need three tricks.

□

Q6432

For problems 493-506, assume IMP scoring.

493   76
           95
           AQJ32
           KJ73

West leads the ♠Q against your 3NT contract. Plan the play.

           AK
           K1073
           654
           AQ109

494   652
           87
           AQ92
           K432

West leads the ♠J against your 3NT contract. Plan the play.

           AQ
           AK43
           J843
           A65

495   J108
           6
           Q7532
           J763

West leads the ♣10 against your 4♠ contract. Plan the play.

           AKQ9765
           KJ42
           6
           A

496   A9
              Q104
              1098752
              A9

West leads the ♠J against your 4♡ contract. You play low from dummy, and your queen wins. How do you continue?

              Q2
              AJ982
              AQJ
              762

497   Dlr: West   AQ63
     Vul: N-S   972
                 K86
                 A102

West leads the ♡K and shifts to the ♢Q. Plan the play.

                 K82
                 J4
                 A9
                 KQ9854

WEST	NORTH	EAST	SOUTH
Pass	1♣	1♡	3♣
3♡	Pass	Pass	3♠
Pass	4♠	All Pass	

498   AQ3
              Q52
              AJ5
              KJ62

West leads the ♠J against your 6NT contract. Plan the play.

              K54
              AK4
              Q103
              A943

499   AK4
K754
J865
AK

West leads the ♣Q against your
6♠ contract. Plan the play.

987653
AQ6
AK
87

500   A953
Q103
K63
543

West leads the ♡2 against your
6♠ contract. Dummy's 10 holds.
Plan the play.

KJ842
AK65
A75
A

501   AJ942
7
AQ5
K542

West leads the ◇J against your
4♡ contract. Plan the play.

5
KQ65432
K62
87

502   A853
                A52
                J65
                KJ3

West leads the ◊K against your 6♠ contract. Plan the play.

                KJ1064
                KQJ6
                --
                AQ54

503   Q93
                J654
                75
                A654

West leads the ♣Q against your 6♠ contract. Plan the play.

                AKJ1087
                A
                AK643
                2

504   Dlr: North   87
       Vul: Both   J42
                     7
                     AKJ7542

West leads the ♠J. Plan the play.

                AQ5
                A853
                KJ93
                63

WEST	NORTH	EAST	SOUTH
---	3♣	Dbl	Redbl
3♠	Pass	Pass	3NT
All Pass			

505   864
           A74
           QJ1053
           92

West leads the ♠J against your 3NT contract. Plan the play.

           AKQ
           K9
           A842
           Q1065

506   76
           AQ3
           765
           KJ432

West leads the ♠4 against your 3NT contract. East plays the 10. Plan the play.

           KJ5
           K54
           A1032
           A65

477   Cash the ace and lead toward the jack.

478   Cash the king and ace before leading to the jack.

479   Lead low from your hand, putting in the 8 if West plays the 7. If West shows out, win in dummy and lead toward the jack.

480   Lead low from dummy toward the queen and jack.

481   Lead low from your hand and play dummy's 9 if West follows low. The best you can do is guard against J-10-8-7-6 with West. (If West splits with that holding, come back to your hand and lead toward the 9.)

482   Lead low from dummy toward the 10.

483   Lead low to the 9 in case West has all the missing cards.

484   Lead low from dummy to your queen. If East follows with the 7 (the crucial case), play the queen. If it loses to the ace and West follows with the 4 on the next round, play dummy's 6.

485   Lead low from dummy toward the 10.

486   Cash the ace before leading toward the queen.

487   Play low from both hands on the first round, saving a trick if West has the singleton ace.

488   Lead low from your hand and play dummy's 10 if West follows low. If West shows out, win the ace and lead toward the queen.

489   Cash the ace, come to your hand and lead toward the jack.

490   Cash the ace and lead toward the jack.

491   Cash the ace and lead toward the 10.

492   Cash the ace, come to your hand and lead toward the 10.

493   Lead a diamond to the ace at the second trick, guarding against the singleton king with East. Later you can lead twice toward dummy's queen and jack.

494   Lead a low diamond to the queen at the second trick. If it loses, cash the ace next. If it wins, come to your hand and lead low to the 9.

495   Lead a heart at the second trick, making sure you get to ruff two hearts in dummy. If instead you cross to dummy with a trump, lead a heart and misguess, a trump return may set you.

496

```
                    A9
                    Q104
                    1098752
                    A9
KJ1075                          8643
65                             K73
K64                            3
J43                            KQ1085
                    Q2
                    AJ982
                    AQJ
                    762
```

In the 1972 Olympiad Open Teams final, one of the winning Italian players executed an unsafety play by leading the ♡A at the second trick. East won the next heart and switched to the ♣K, ducked, and another club to the ace. Now if declarer drew trumps, he would lose two clubs, a diamond and a trump. If he led to the ◊A to ruff his third club, he would be stuck in dummy — the defense would get a diamond ruff.

Declarer could have saved himself by leading a low trump at trick two.

497

                    AQ63
                    972
                    K86
                    A102

    10954   J7
    KQ8   A10653
    QJ104   7532
    J7   63

                    K82
                    J4
                    A9
                    KQ9854

In the 1981 Venice Trophy, a U.S. player won the diamond switch with the ace, gave up a heart, won the next diamond, ruffed a heart and cashed three rounds of trumps. When East discarded, declarer tried to run the clubs to discard dummy's diamond, but West ruffed the third round and cashed a diamond. Down one.

The safer (and winning) play would have been a low trump from both hands at the third trick. The defenders can cash a heart, but declarer can win the next trick, draw trumps and run the clubs.

498   Take an early diamond finesse. If it loses, you need four club tricks — lead low to the jack without cashing the ace (in case West holds the singleton queen). If the diamond finesse wins, you need only three club tricks. Cash the king and lead low toward your hand, playing the 9 if the defenders follow with low cards.

499   Come to your hand with a diamond and lead a low trump, playing low from dummy if West follows with the 2.

500   Lead a club to the ace and a low spade toward dummy, planning to play dummy's 9 if West follows low. If instead West shows out, you can pick up the trumps with two finesses against East and lose one diamond.

The actual declarer led a spade to the king at the second trick — an unsafety play — and West showed out. The contract could no longer be made.

501   Win the ◇K and lead a club to the king. If it loses, you must find East with A-x of trumps. If the ♣K wins, lead dummy's trump and play low from your hand, saving a trick if West has the singleton ace.

502   Ruff the first trick and lay down the ♠K. This assures the contract. (If West shows out, you will pass the ♠J to East next.)

In actual play, declarer led a spade to the ace at trick two, and East showed out. When West won the ♠Q, a second diamond lead promoted the ♠9 by forcing declarer to ruff with an honor.

503

	Q93	
	J654	
	75	
	A654	
654		2
K1083		Q972
2		QJ1098
QJ987		K103
	AKJ1087	
	A	
	AK643	
	2	

Win the ♣A, lead a diamond to the ace and concede a diamond. If East returns a trump, you win and ruff your two low diamonds with the ♠9 and ♠Q. The ◇K is the 12th trick.

If you try to make seven by taking the ◇AK, the 5-1 diamond break beats you. West ruffs the second diamond and returns a trump, leaving you a trick short.

504   Declarer should win the first trick and lead a club, planning to play low from dummy (even if West plays the queen).

```
                    87
                    J42
                    7
                    AKJ7542
        J1043                   K962
        97                      KQ106
        642                     AQ1085
        Q1098                   --
                    AQ5
                    A853
                    KJ93
                    63
```

505   Win the first trick and lead the ♢A and another diamond. You can't afford to cross to the ♡A to take the diamond finesse. What if diamonds are 4-0?

506
```
                    76
                    AQ3
                    765
                    KJ432
        AQ942                   1083
        10762                   J98
        J84                     KQ9
        Q                       10987
                    KJ5
                    K54
                    A1032
                    A65
```

Win the ♠J and lead a low club. If West follows low, you will play the king and ace, trying to keep East out of the lead. As the cards lie, East's 10-9-8-7 are worth an entry, but you can make the contract by letting West's ♣Q hold.

II. Play 'em Right

507   AJ543   You need three tricks.

      ☐

      108

508   AJ8542   You need six tricks.

      ☐

      Q973

509   A642   You need four tricks.

      ☐

      KJ103

510   Q642   You need four tricks.

      ☐

      KJ873

511   AK103   You need four tricks.

      ☐

      Q2

512   A876543   You need six tricks.

□

J10

513   A432   You need four tricks.

□

KQ10

514   AJ32   You need three tricks.

□

K9

515   AK932   You need five tricks.

□

J8764

516   AQ92   You need three tricks.

□

J3

517   AK1092   You need four tricks.

□

43

518   Q109632   You need five tricks.

□

A

519   A10432   You need four tricks.

□

K9

520   KQJ943   You need five tricks.

□

2

521   Q10987   You need four tricks.

□

A4

522   A102   You need two tricks.

□

Q43

523   J105432   You need four tricks.

□

A

524   A95432   You need five tricks.

☐

J6

525   A109832   You need four tricks.

☐

4

526   Q97654   You need four tricks.

☐

K3

527   AKQ87   You need four tricks.

☐

104

528   A10653   You need four tricks.

☐

Q974

529   A1098   You need three tricks.

☐

Q432

530   A10832   You need five tricks.

☐

Q654

For problems 531-536, assume IMP scoring.

531   765
AK5
876
J843

               West leads the ♠Q against your
3NT contract. Plan the play.

AK3
76
A103
AQ752

532   A106
Q32
AK65
K32

               West leads the ♡J against your
7♠ contract. Plan the play.

KQ972
AK4
Q87
A4

533   765
              A5
              AJ54
              AK65

West leads the ◊Q against your 6♡ contract. Plan the play.

              AK
              K108732
              6
              QJ32

534   9742
              KQ753
              K5
              K7

West leads the ◊10. East wins the ace and returns a diamond to dummy's king. Plan the play.

              KQ86
              2
              QJ4
              AQJ93

WEST	NORTH	EAST	SOUTH
Pass	Pass	Pass	1♣
Pass	1♡	Pass	1♠
Pass	3♠	Pass	4♠
All Pass			

535   Q10543
           AK4
           AKQ2
           5

West leads the ♢J against your 3NT contract. Plan the play.

           92
           Q52
           76
           AQ10942

536   AQ7
           76
           K43
           AJ1054

West leads the ♡J against your 6NT contract. You win and elect to lead the ♠2 — 3, queen, 5. How do you continue?

           J942
           AK
           A652
           KQ6

507   The best chance is to lead low from dummy to your 8.

508   Lead the queen for a finesse, which saves a trick if West has K-10-6.

509   Cash the ace and finesse through East. You can pick up Q-9-x-x with East but not with West.

510   Play the queen on the first round in case East has A-10-9-7.

511   Cash the queen and finesse the 10.

512   Lead the jack and run it, gaining if East has the singleton 9.

513   Cash the king and queen.

514   Lead low to the 9. If it loses to the 10, cash the king and ace.

515   Lead the jack, intending to win dummy's ace if West plays the 5 smoothly. The jack tempts West to cover with Q-10-5.

516   Lead low to the jack. If it loses to the king, lead to the 9 next.

517   Lead low to the 9. If it loses to an honor, lead low to the 10 next.

518   Lead the queen after cashing the ace, hoping to pin the doubleton jack.

519   Lead low to the 9. This play is also correct with A-10-x-x opposite K-9.

520   Lead low to the king and continue with the queen if it wins. If dummy had K-Q-J-9-x, you would finesse the 9 on the first round.

521   The best play is to lead the queen.

522   Lead low to the queen. If it loses to the king, lead to the 10 next.

523   After cashing the ace, lead low; this gains against K-x or Q-x.

524   Lead low toward the jack. If East puts up the king or queen, lead the jack next, hoping to pin East's 10. If East plays the 10 on the first round, lead to the ace next (paying off if East falsecards with the 10 from 10-x.)

525   Lead low to the 10 and cash the ace next.

526   Lead the 9, intending to play low from your hand if East plays low. This play gains if West has the singleton 8.

527   The best play is to cash an honor in dummy, then return to your hand and lead the 10, intending to play low from dummy if West plays low.

528   Cash the ace and lead toward the queen.

529   Lead the queen. If it loses to the king, lead to the 10 next.

530   Lead the queen, hoping East has the singleton jack or West fails to cover with K-x.

531   Since you need only four club tricks, go to dummy with a heart and lead the ♣J in case East has K-10-9-6. This is better than low to the jack because it picks up an overtrick when the king doubleton is onside.

532   Cash the ace first in case East has J-8-5-4-3.

533   Lead the 10 from your hand. If West plays the 4 or 6, play low from dummy. If West plays the 9, jack or queen, win the ace and return the 5, planning to play the 7 if East plays low. This position is similar to the one discussed in problem #526.

534   Lead the ♡K at the third trick. If West wins the ace and returns, say, a diamond, ruff and lead a trump to your king, playing East for A-x or A-x-x. However, if East wins the ♡A, West must hold the ♠A, since East would have opened the bidding in third seat with three aces. In that case you must get to dummy and lead a spade to the 8, hoping East has the jack and 10.

535   Win the first trick and lead a club to the queen. This play gains over leading a club to the 10 when West has J-x.

536   Presumably West has the ♠K, since East would have been eager to win and return a heart. Return to your hand and lead the ♠J. This play gains if East started with 8-5 doubleton; it breaks even otherwise.

QUICK QUIZ

Famous Pairs

Match up the following successful partnerships.

537	Bobby Goldman	Richard Pavlicek
538	Jacqui Mitchell	Victor Mitchell
539	Pietro Forquet	Chuck Burger
540	Carol Sanders	Sami Kehela
541	Bob Hamman	Lew Stansby
542	Sam Stayman	Ed Manfield
543	Chip Martel	Judi Radin
544	Kit Woolsey	Mark Lair
545	Alvin Roth	Beth Palmer
546	Hugh Ross	Bobby Wolff
547	Bill Root	Norman Kay
548	Kathie Wei	Larry Cohen
549	Lynn Deas	Eric Rodwell
550	Eric Murray	Peter Pender
551	James Cayne	Paul Soloway
552	Mike Passell	Ronnie Rubin
553	Mike Becker	Benito Garozzo
554	Edgar Kaplan	Amalya Kearse
555	Marty Bergen	Betty Ann Kennedy
556	Jeff Meckstroth	Barbara (Rappaport) Haberman

537	Goldman-Soloway
538	Mitchell-Kearse
539	Forquet-Garozzo
540	Sanders-Kennedy
541	Hamman-Wolff
542	Stayman-Mitchell
543	Martel-Stansby
544	Woolsey-Manfield
545	Roth-Rappaport
546	Ross-Pender
547	Root-Pavlicek
548	Wei-Radin
549	Deas-Palmer
550	Murray-Kehela
551	Cayne-Burger
552	Passell-Lair
553	Becker-Rubin
554	Kaplan-Kay
555	Bergen-Cohen
556	Meckstroth-Rodwell

Crystal-Ball Gazing — Constructive Auctions

You'll be shown an auction and five hands. Circle the hand your partner is most likely to hold for his bidding. (Assume he has bid correctly, for once.)

	YOU	PARD					
557	1♡	2♣	Q753	A103	K853	A963	A64
	2♡	2♠	K5	K6	Q5	KJ2	K3
	3♣	3♡	AJ3	QJ8	A5	4	964
			A1062	KJ653	KQ953	AQ1064	A10653
			(a)	(b)	(c)	(d)	(e)
558	—	1♡	75	AQ	A2	K5	—
	1NT	2◇	AQ10753	QJ1098	AKQ1076	AQ10872	KQ1064
	3◇	3♡	AQ64	K653	Q763	AQ73	AQ1065
			3	KQ	Q	4	K53
			(a)	(b)	(c)	(d)	(e)
559	—	Pass	J3	765	K43	632	54
	1♡	3♣	104	653	54	54	QJ73
			J43	KQ	2	Q1065	54
			AKQ1042	AKJ32	KQJ9653	AKQ4	AK1064
			(a)	(b)	(c)	(d)	(e)
560	1♡	3◇	AK43	A105	A	A105	A105
	3♡	3♠	2	K9	65	KQ3	KJ3
			AK653	AKJ64	AKQJ432	AKJ54	AK654
			KJ9	QJ4	Q32	65	54
			(a)	(b)	(c)	(d)	(e)
561	1♡	1♠	A10643	AQ543	AQ864	AQJ76	K10654
	1NT	2♡	K54	K3	K93	AQ4	J43
			54	765	43	54	43
			954	953	J64	543	1064
			(a)	(b)	(c)	(d)	(e)

	YOU	PARD					

562

YOU	PARD					
--	1♡	KQ5	KJ4	1064	KJ3	10653
1♠	2♠	AK1064	AK1064	AK10653	AK10843	AKQ54
2NT	3♡	J3	2	7	2	3
		1064	Q1086	KJ2	1076	QJ3
		(a)	(b)	(c)	(d)	(e)

563

YOU	PARD					
--	1♣	A753	A653	AJ85	AK65	J753
1♡	1♠	K64	KQ6	KQ5	1054	KQ7
1NT	2♡	J9	Q5	3	A2	2
		AQ64	AQ64	KQ953	AK83	AQ753
		(a)	(b)	(c)	(d)	(e)

564

YOU	PARD					
1♣	1♡	K54	7	74	5	6
2♣	2♢	Q1075	AK1042	Q1076	AQJ105	AK1042
2♡	3♣	AK6	KQ8	AQ87	KJ54	K943
		Q106	Q1054	Q106	1076	Q86
		(a)	(b)	(c)	(d)	(e)

565

YOU	PARD					
--	1♡	A104	A10	A10	863	A103
2♢	2NT	AQJ106	AQJ94	AJ953	AQ1065	AJ973
3♣	3♢	Q3	J54	KQ3	K54	Q54
3♡	3♠	1076	K54	765	AJ	K3
		(a)	(b)	(c)	(d)	(e)

566

YOU	PARD					
--	1♠	AK653	AK754	AQ853	AK875	AK543
2♡	3♣	K3	J104	KQ9	K4	KJ3
3♢	3♡	76	3	43	76	2
		KJ82	KJ82	A65	AQJ2	AJ104
		(a)	(b)	(c)	(d)	(e)

	YOU	PARD					
567							
	2♣	2◇	87	1076	87	76	54
	2♡	3♡	KJ83	J654	K65	K1076	QJ
			875	876	762	AJ65	AQ9763
			9542	643	109654	765	864
			(a)	(b)	(c)	(d)	(e)
568							
	--	1◇	Q92	AK3	AJ3	Q9	A10
	1♠	2♣	54	5	3	Q4	54
	2♡	2♠	AQ74	AQ753	AJ1053	KQJ3	AK764
			AJ103	K853	Q952	A9743	KJ84
			(a)	(b)	(c)	(d)	(e)
569							
	--	1♡	64	Q3	Q4	8	Q64
	3♡ *	4♣	KQJ963	KQ9642	Q109652	K97542	KJ953
	4◇	5♣	K74	54	K4	KJ7	64
			AK	AKQ	AK5	AK3	AKJ
	* Forcing		(a)	(b)	(c)	(d)	(e)
570							
	--	1◇	AQ75	AK103	AK10	AKJ5	AQ5
	1♡	2♠	Q3	--	76	Q82	KJ53
	3♡	4♣	AK953	AKJ94	AQ964	AQ964	AKJ82
			A3	KJ83	AQ8	A	5
			(a)	(b)	(c)	(d)	(e)
571							
	--	1NT	A1074	AK64	Q1065	KQJ6	KQ85
	3♡	4♡	K64	K964	A85	J84	K75
	5♣	6♡	AK93	A85	AKJ5	AKJ3	AQ53
			Q6	K4	Q6	J4	Q9
			(a)	(b)	(c)	(d)	(e)

	YOU	PARD	(a)	(b)	(c)	(d)	(e)
572							
	—	1♠	A10832	KJ953	AQ1076	AJ653	AQ654
	1NT	2◇	A7	Q6	K4	--	K7
	3◇	4◇	AJ953	AKQ6	KJ104	KQ853	KQ1053
			7	76	A6	Q76	4
			(a)	(b)	(c)	(d)	(e)
573							
	1♡	1♠	AJ54	A853	KJ753	AJ653	QJ103
	2♣	2◇	K32	AK8	AQ7	1053	K53
	2NT	4♡	K873	K653	AJ63	AK85	A108
			76	65	6	4	Q103
			(a)	(b)	(c)	(d)	(e)
574							
	1♡	1NT	J83	A105	K106	AQ8	A97
	2♣	2NT	KJ3	Q6	6	Q4	5
			A764	K7532	Q108652	Q1083	K8532
			J93	1065	Q76	9742	Q754
			(a)	(b)	(c)	(d)	(e)
575							
	1♡	2♣	K105	8	75	87	76
	2♡	3◇	J	Q53	Q6	K5	K54
	3♡	4♡	K1084	A954	AQ65	AQ43	AJ6
			AQJ53	AK853	AJ543	AKJ65	KQ542
			(a)	(b)	(c)	(d)	(e)
576							
	—	1◇	KQ5	AQ53	A753	10432	AK5
	1♡	2♡	A74	K64	K653	AK2	AQ7
	2NT	3♠	AJ1064	A10763	AQ64	A873	J97532
			73	Q	4	Q6	5
			(a)	(b)	(c)	(d)	(e)

557 a. would respond 1♠ and bid 4♡ over 2♡.
     b. would bid 3NT over 2♡; better yet is 2NT, if played forcing.
     c. is correct.
     d. would jump to 4♡ over 3♣.
     e. isn't strong enough for the sequence; would raise 2♡ to 3♡.

558 a. would rebid 2♡ over 1NT.
     b. would raise 1NT to 2NT (or rebid 3NT over 3◊).
     c. would jump to 3♡ over 1NT.
     d. is correct.
     e. would bid 4♣ over 3◊.

559 a. would respond 2♣, although this used to be a perfect passed-hand
        jump before most experts adopted the style that passed-hand jumps
        promise a fit for opener.
     b. would open the bidding.
     c. might open 3♣; would respond 2♣.
     d. would respond 2♣, or 1NT, if "forcing."
     e. is correct.

560 a. would respond only 2◊, saving room to find the right strain.
     b. would bid 3NT over 3♡.
     c. would bid 4◊ over 3♡.
     d. is correct.
     e. is a very light jump shift and would merely raise 3♡ to 4♡.

561 a. would raise 1♡ to 2♡, assuming we play five-card majors.
     b. would pass 1NT.
     c. is correct.
     d. would bid 3♡ (forcing) over 1NT.
     e. would raise directly to 2♡ or pass the opening bid (depends on mood).

562 a. would pass 2NT.
     b. would bid 3♣ over 2NT.
     c. would rebid 2♡ over 1♠ with bad spades.
     d. is correct.
     e. would return to 3♠ over 2NT.

563   a. would pass 1NT.
       b. would open 1NT.
       c. is correct.
       d. would raise 1NT to 2NT with bad hearts.
       e. is a minimum but good for hearts; should raise 1♡ to 2♡.

564   a. would bid 3NT over 2♣.
       b. would jump to 4♣ over 2♡.
       c. would raise 2♣ to 3♣, limiting the hand.
       d. would bid 4♡ over 2♡.
       e. is correct.

565   a. would bid 2♡ over 2◇.
       b. would bid 4♡ over 3♡.
       c. would raise 2◇ to 3◇.
       d. would avoid the 2NT rebid with nothing in spades.
       e. is correct.

566   a. would rebid 2♠ over 2♡.
       b. would raise 2♡ to 3♡.
       c. would raise 2♡ to 4♡.
       d. is correct.
       e. would jump to 4♡ over 3◇.

567   a. would raise 2♡ to 4♡.
       b. would bid 2NT (or give an artificial second negative) over 2♡, then
          take a cheap heart preference next or pass a 3♡ rebid.
       c. would bid 2NT (or give an artificial second negative) over 2♡, then
          jump to 4♡ next or raise a 3♡ rebid to 4♡.
       d. is correct.
       e. would bid 3◇ over 2♣.

568   a. should open 1♣, but regardless should raise 1♠ to 2♠.
       b. would jump to 3♠ over 2♡.
       c. would raise 1♠ to 2♠.
       d. If we open 1◇ and rebid 2♣ (which we shouldn't), we bid 2NT
          over 2♡.
       e. is correct.

569 a. would bid 5♡ over 4◇, *insisting* on slam if responder had a spade control.
     b. is correct.
     c. would bid 4♡ over 4◇; not strong enough for a second encouraging move.
     d. would Blackwood over 3♡ or 4◇.
     e. would bid 4♡ over 3♡; too weak for a slam try.

570 a. would raise 3♡ to 4♡.
     b. would bid 3NT over 3♡.
     c. would jump to 2NT over 1♡. (In many partnerships, opener would jump to 2NT even with one more spade and one less diamond.)
     d. is correct.
     e. would raise hearts directly, probably by means of a 4♣ splinter bid.

571 a. is correct.
     b. would make an advance cuebid of 3♠ over 3♡.
     c. is not strong enough to jump to slam (especially with no spade control), but would cuebid 5◇ over 5♣.
     d. should sign off in 5♡. This hand is not slam-oriented, with four jacks and no cards in partner's suits. If you *must* bid 5◇ here on any hand with the ◇A, how can partner ever judge what to do?
     e. should bid 5◇ over 5♣. This is an average-plus hand. You can't go past 5♡, but can cuebid under 5♡ to show some interest.

572 a. would jump to 5◇ over 3◇. Responder is likely to have a singleton spade, so there is no wastage in the spade suit.
     b. would pass 3◇. Opener has a near-minimum and the wrong spade holding.
     c. would bid 3NT over 3◇.
     d. would try for game with 4♣, letting responder judge the fit.
     e. is correct. Note that opener is likely to be 5-5; otherwise, he would have a more descriptive game try.

573   a. would jump to 3♡ over 2♣.
       b. would jump to 4♡ over 2♣, showing strong trumps.
       c. is correct.
       d. would bid only 3♡ (forcing) over 2NT, because of the weak hearts.
       e. would raise 2NT to 3NT.

574   a. should prefer a raise to 2♡ to a 1NT response.
       b. would return to 2♡ over 2♣.
       c. would bid 2◊ over 2♣.
       d. is correct.
       e. would raise 2♣ to 3♣. This is not a hand for notrump, with no heart
          fit and prime cards in spades and diamonds.

575   a. would bid 3NT over 2♡; even better is 2NT, if played forcing.
       b. would Blackwood or try 4♠ (splinter bid) over 3♡.
       c. is correct.
       d. would bid 5♡ over 3♡, demanding slam opposite a spade control.
       e. would raise 2♡ to 4♡.

576   a. would raise 2NT to 3NT.
       b. would bid 1♠ over 1♡.
       c. would jump to 4♡ over 2NT.
       d. would pass 2NT.
       e. is correct, we guess. This is a rare sequence. Partner must be short in
          clubs (he bid three suits) with only three-card heart support (he failed
          to rebid his hearts); and the fact he did not rebid 1♠ on the first
          round of the auction limits him to three cards in spades. (Yes, he
          might have four weak spades and three strong hearts, as in hand "d,"
          but only if balanced. On unbalanced hands he can afford to rebid 1♠
          and later support hearts.)

Crystal-Ball Gazing — Competitive Auctions

Neither side vulnerable at IMPs. You'll be shown a competitive auction and five hands. Circle the hand your partner, SOUTH, is most likely to hold for his bidding. You can still assume that he's in good form — his bidding is reasonable, if not perfect.

				?
577	WEST	NORTH	EAST	SOUTH
	--	--	3♣	Dbl
	Pass	3♠	Pass	3NT

K54	K3	93	J43	Q54
AK3	A93	AJ5	A953	AKQ4
KQJ64	AJ9543	AKQ1076	AQ3	AQJ53
A3	K3	K3	KJ2	A
(a)	(b)	(c)	(d)	(e)

				?
578	WEST	NORTH	EAST	SOUTH
	--	1♡	2♣	2♡
	3♣	4♣	5♣	Pass

8	A7	Q1063	J106	654
Q10753	Q865	J64	Q953	Q962
QJ965	Q1054	K942	K64	AJ1053
76	654	76	K105	5
(a)	(b)	(c)	(d)	(e)

	WEST	NORTH	EAST	SOUTH
579	--	--	--	1♣
	Pass	1♡	1♠	3NT

(a)	(b)	(c)	(d)	(e)
KJ4	A5	A6	AQ94	K65
Q6	KJ8	A7	5	J
A106	AJ75	763	AKJ7	A5
AKJ83	AQ92	AKJ953	A1065	AKQ10763

	WEST	NORTH	EAST	SOUTH
580	--	--	1♣	Pass
	1♡	Pass	2♡	Pass
	Pass	2♠	Pass	3♠

(a)	(b)	(c)	(d)	(e)
J62	AK5	KJ93	AJ94	AJ84
A65	Q3	8653	J753	J764
K764	QJ63	Q5	K9653	AK5
Q74	Q432	AQ5	--	76

	WEST	NORTH	EAST	SOUTH
581	--	--	1♣	Pass
	1♦	Pass	1♡	1♠

(a)	(b)	(c)	(d)	(e)
KQ1053	KJ10853	AQ84	AQ95	AK106
87	65	6	K64	K5
KQ96	QJ94	KQ65	Q84	65
84	5	K1054	Q105	KQ953

582

?

WEST	NORTH	EAST	SOUTH
—	1♠	2♡	3♡
Pass	3♠	Pass	4♣

Q63	Q76	Q964	Q953	K9752
7	A4	7	76	A7
K763	K864	K943	KJ3	76
AKJ63	AJ64	AK63	AK54	AKJ4
(a)	(b)	(c)	(d)	(e)

583

?

WEST	NORTH	EAST	SOUTH
—	—	Pass	Pass
1♠	2♣	2♡	4♣

65	A764	4	A864	7
A83	76	J7	6	876
K653	J75	QJ953	Q1064	AQ1062
A1053	10764	K10853	J763	J953
(a)	(b)	(c)	(d)	(e)

584

?

WEST	NORTH	EAST	SOUTH
—	—	—	1◇
1♠	Pass	Pass	1NT

KJ5	KJ43	A5	AQ7	K5
J5	76	AQ94	K93	A10
AK963	KQ65	AK765	AQ74	AKQJ74
A106	A104	J5	KJ3	J105
(a)	(b)	(c)	(d)	(e)

585	WEST	NORTH	EAST	SOUTH
				?
	—	—	—	1♠
	Dbl	Redbl	2♣	Pass
	Pass	Dbl	Pass	2♡

(a)	(b)	(c)	(d)	(e)
AJ1075	AJ1076	AJ1076	AKJ986	AK964
KQ943	KJ93	AK1075	J742	AQ93
Q7	A7	K6	A7	Q6
4	J7	7	6	76
(a)	(b)	(c)	(d)	(e)

586	WEST	NORTH	EAST	SOUTH
				?
	—	—	—	1♢
	Pass	1♡	1♠	2♣

A8	5	Q6	AQ94	65
65	KQ6	AQ	—	6
KJ964	AJ874	AJ94	AK843	AJ953
AJ93	K1065	KJ862	AJ74	AK863
(a)	(b)	(c)	(d)	(e)

587	WEST	NORTH	EAST	SOUTH
				?
	—	1NT	Pass	Pass
	2♡	Pass	Pass	2♠

J10542	J10763	AQ973	KQ94	AJ64
652	76	65	76	874
Q753	J763	Q1064	Q973	653
6	54	65	1032	1064
(a)	(b)	(c)	(d)	(e)

588

WEST	NORTH	EAST	SOUTH
—	1♡	1♠	2♣
Pass	2◊	Pass	3♡
Pass	4♡	Pass	5♣
Pass	5◊	Pass	5♡

				?
76	963	76	7	7
AQ8	KQ6	KQ6	KQ5	KJ63
KJ6	87	KJ4	Q75	Q764
AKJ53	AKJ74	AQJ64	AKJ652	AKJ3
(a)	(b)	(c)	(d)	(e)

589

WEST	NORTH	EAST	SOUTH
—	1♣	1♠	Pass
2♠	Pass	Pass	2NT

				?
8	87	7	AQ7	KJ84
K963	63	Q9753	765	A763
Q10764	KJ953	QJ9653	K1064	QJ953
K64	KJ43	6	J54	—
(a)	(b)	(c)	(d)	(e)

590

WEST	NORTH	EAST	SOUTH
1♡	Dbl	Pass	2◊
Pass	Pass	2♡	2♠

				?
Q942	Q953	KJ83	Q963	AQ5
654	5	65	65	65
KJ86	KJ763	AJ532	J8652	Q10653
76	764	54	76	654
(a)	(b)	(c)	(d)	(e)

				?
591	WEST	NORTH	EAST	SOUTH
	—	—	1♡	Pass
	Pass	1♠	Pass	2◊

(a)	(b)	(c)	(d)	(e)
A54	AQ	A74	J5	K4
654	Q75	A65	AQ7	AQ1085
AKJ864	AK964	AJ764	KJ652	QJ1095
5	J53	76	K105	8
(a)	(b)	(c)	(d)	(e)

				?
592	WEST	NORTH	EAST	SOUTH
	—	1♡	Pass	2♡
	Pass	Pass	Dbl	Pass

(a)	(b)	(c)	(d)	(e)
AQ97	8	54	K65	6
J73	Q864	Q87	Q84	Q864
65	KJ763	AJ9532	K642	765
Q1063	543	54	543	AQ765
(a)	(b)	(c)	(d)	(e)

				?
593	WEST	NORTH	EAST	SOUTH
	—	1◊	Dbl	1♡
	1♠	Pass	2♠	3◊

(a)	(b)	(c)	(d)	(e)
863	K54	Q106	6	62
J953	A764	J964	J763	AQ964
AQ76	KJ64	Q953	AJ853	KJ63
65	76	K6	654	65
(a)	(b)	(c)	(d)	(e)

594

	WEST	NORTH	EAST	SOUTH
	--	--	--	1NT
	2◇	Pass	Pass	Dbl

(a)	(b)	(c)	(d)	(e)
KJ6	A76	AKJ5	K65	Q86
AQ76	AK5	Q763	AKJ74	AQ6
K6	KJ63	A7	A6	AJ5
QJ94	Q84	K54	J63	KQJ5

595

	WEST	NORTH	EAST	SOUTH
	--	--	--	1◇
	Pass	1♡	Dbl	Redbl

(a)	(b)	(c)	(d)	(e)
76	7	A85	7	AQ87
KQ6	KQ87	KJ	A54	54
AK653	AK852	AK9763	AQ873	AK763
J54	1064	43	AQ105	A5

596

	WEST	NORTH	EAST	SOUTH
	--	--	1♠	2♣
	2♠	Pass	Pass	2NT

(a)	(b)	(c)	(d)	(e)
KQ7	76	K6	--	864
1063	5	KJ63	KJ4	--
A7	KJ72	A4	A953	AQ94
AKJ64	KJ10865	KJ965	AQ8652	AKJ872

577   a. is correct. South suggests a tolerance for the majors since he did not overcall 3NT directly.

       b. would overcall 3◊.

       c. would overcall 3NT.

       d. should pass 3♣.

       e. would bid 4♣ or 4◊ over 3♠. This hand has too much slam potential to bid 3NT.

578   a. would raise to 4♡ over 2♣.

       b. is correct. There are no wasted club values. South can encourage North to bid 5♡. Note that pass is 100% forcing because North cuebid.

       c. would double 5♣. With this minimum raise, South should discourage partner from bidding on.

       d. would double 5♣. This is a maximum raise, but the ♣K is a defensive value and is probably wasted for offense.

       e. is unusually strong for a single raise. South would bid 5♡ — or perhaps cuebid 5◊ — over 5♣.

579   a. would jump to 2NT over 1♠.

       b. would bid 2◊ over 1♠, planning to show the heart support next. Any notrump bid is premature with this hand.

       c. would jump to 3♣ over 1♠.

       d. would double 1♠ for penalty.

       e. is correct. The jump to 3NT warns North not to correct to hearts. If hearts were a likely spot, South would bid slowly.

580   a. would pass 2♠ in a flash.

       b. would pass 2♠. This hand is stronger, but all that means is that North will be weaker. South has no unexpectedly good distribution, and his ♣Q and ♡Q may be wasted.

       c. is correct. Four trumps and sound, useful values. If South has a decent hand with a useful feature (such as a singleton heart) — something like Q10xxx, x, AJxx, xxx — he should bid 4♠.

       d. would raise to 4♠. The club void is a feature North can't possibly visualize.

       e. would double 1♣.

581 a. would overcall 1♠ directly.

b. would jump to 2♠, preemptive, over 1♣.

c. would double over 1♡. Some players might overcall 1◇ or 1♠ over 1♣ with this hand.

d. would pass throughout.

e. is correct. The most logical explanation for South's delayed entry is that he trapped at his first turn with good clubs.

582 a. would bid 3♣ over 2♡. The spade support isn't good enough to commit the hand to spades — a club slam is possible.

b. would settle for a raise to 4♠ over 3♠.

c. is a possible hand, but many players would jump to 4♡ over 2♡ to show a spade fit with a singleton heart.

d. might bid 3♡ in some styles as the only strong action available. However, again, South would settle for a raise to 4♠ over 3♠.

e. is correct.

583 a. would cuebid 2♠, showing a strong hand with clubs.

b. would pass over 2♡. South has nothing to gain by raising clubs.

c. would jump to 5♣. The opponents surely have a game, so South should save immediately, putting them to a guess.

d. is correct. Here South has a couple of possible defensive tricks. He can suggest a save, but he must not save on his own. North can save if his hand is suitable.

e. would raise to 3♣ or, even better, bid 3◇ over 2♡ as a lead director. To risk this bid, South is likely to have a club fit.

584 a. would open 1NT.

b. would pass out 1♠. North doesn't have spades and couldn't bid a suit, raise diamonds or make a negative double.

c. would reopen with a double.

d. is correct. South's sequence shows a hand slightly too strong for a 1NT opening.

e. would jump to 2NT over 1♠ with eight possible playing tricks.

585   a. would bid 2♡ directly over 2♣, showing a weak two-suiter.

        b. would pass 2♣ doubled.

        c. is correct.

        d. would bid 2♠ directly over 2♣.

        e. would pass 2♣ doubled.

586   a. would pass 1♠. No excuse for a free bid.

        b. would raise to 2♡ over 1♠. If West is about to raise spades, South must get in his heart raise now. If the hand were slightly stronger — x, KQx, AKxxx, Axxx — 2♣ would be correct.

        c. would open 1NT.

        d. would double 1♠ for penalty.

        e. is correct. Most modern players agree that free bids are desirable with a long suit or a two-suiter even without extra high-card strength.

587   a. would bid 2♠ over 1NT.

        b. should bid 2♠ over 1NT. 5-4-2-2 hands generally play better with a trump suit.

        c. is good enough to invite game. South would try 2♣ over 1NT, planning to bid 2♠ over 2♢ or 2♡ by North.

        d. is correct. South is likely to have only four spades and should have enough strength to make 2NT playable if North can't stand spades.

        e. is too weak to act over 2♡.

588   a. would bid 5♡ over 4♡, *insisting* on slam if North has a spade control.

        b. is too weak for a slam try and would pass 4♡.

        c. is correct. Enough for a mild slam try, but not enough to drive to slam opposite a spade control, as in hand (a).

        d. would bid 4♠ over 4♡, or 6♡ over 5♢.

        e. would cuebid 2♠ (or, even better, jump to 3♠) over 1♠.

589   a. would make a negative double over 1♠.

       b. would raise clubs earlier.

       c. is correct.

       d. would bid 1NT over 1♠.

       e. probably would have acted earlier, perhaps with a negative double or 2◇ bid over 1♠. If South chose to pass over 1♠, he would double now — presumably for penalty, since 2NT is available for takeout.

590   a. would respond 1♠ to the double, showing the major suit.

       b. is a possible hand. Anticipating heart competition, South might show his diamonds first, keeping an economical spade bid in reserve. Nevertheless, to bid this way is ambiguous, and many Souths would still respond 1♠.

       c. is worth a jump to 2♠ in response to the double.

       d. would respond 1♠. The hand is too weak to bid twice.

       e. is correct. South is likely to have three good spades.

591   a. would overcall 2◇ over 1♡.

       b. would overcall 1NT over 1♡.

       c. would raise spades or cuebid 2♡ over 1♠.

       d. would bid 2NT over 1♠.

       e. is correct.

592   a. would redouble.

       b. would reraise to 3♡ over the double, trying to shut out the spades.

       c. would bid 3◇ over the double.

       d. is correct. This is a normal raise.

       e. is worth at least a limit raise to 3♡ originally.

593   a. should avoid a heart bid with such a poor suit. Since the takeout doubler probably has hearts, a raise to 2◊ is more realistic.

       b. has the right strength and pattern to redouble.

       c. should bid 1NT over the double. Again, since the opponents may compete, giving a general description of the hand is more important than showing the hearts.

       d. should jump to 3◊ over the double.

       e. is correct. Although this hand is strong enough to redouble, it's better to start describing the offensive features.

594   a. would pass 2◊. This hand is too weak to act again.

       b. would pass 2◊. This hand is maximum, but the diamond honors lie in front of the diamond bidder and are therefore discounted. South could double for penalty with this hand if *East* had balanced with 2◊.

       c. is correct. A double *in front of* the diamond bidder is for takeout and suggests a maximum.

       d. would bid 2♡ over 2◊.

       e. is too strong to open 1NT. (19 points — count `em.)

595   a. would raise to 2♡, preparing for competition.

       b. would raise to 3♡.

       c. would rebid 2◊.

       d. would rebid 2♣. A redouble is shortsighted — since the opponents may compete in spades, South should start describing his pattern.

       e. is correct, although this is not the only possible hand for South. (He could have a strong, relatively balanced hand with heart support, for example.)

596   a. would bid 1NT over 1♠.

       b. would jump to 3♣, preemptive, over 1♠. This hand is too weak to overcall 2♣ and certainly too weak to bid again if it did.

       c. would double 1♠ and probably not act again.

       d. would overcall 2♣ but would reopen with a double of 2♠.

       e. is correct. South's sequence suggests a good hand with six clubs and four diamonds.

History Lesson

597   True or false? Hoyle of "according to Hoyle" is an authority on gambling who currently lives in Las Vegas.

598   Name the six players who originally formed the U.S. Aces.

599   Where did the Acol system get its name?

600   How was a U.S. Open Pair Championship decided two days after the event was over?

601   Who was Sarah Battle?

602   What world-famous figure said that he first felt God's influence in his life while playing bridge at an English resort?

603   At the concluding banquet at the 1956 World Championship, it was announced that records of the bidding and play would be on sale at the door. What was Charles Goren's comment?

604   Why was that immortal squad from Italy called the Blue Team?

605   What player became a Life Master in a record 9 weeks?

606   What's the origin of the term "kibitzer?"

607   Who devised the first forcing club system?

608   Was Ely Culbertson American or Russian?

609   True or false? Culbertson never became an ACBL Life Master.

610   What was Culbertson's reply when, in 1933, a reporter asked, "How did you get ahead of all those other bridge experts?"

611   Who was the first woman Life Master?

612   True or false? Harold Vanderbilt, in transit of the Panama Canal on the cruise ship *Finlandia* in late 1925, devised the scoring method that led to the rise of contract bridge.

613   What's the "pitch count?"

614   What is the 7-5-3-2-1 point count called?

615   Who was Bryant McCampbell?

616   What's the link between bridge and the Russian space program?

617   Jo Culbertson was Mrs. Josephine Murphy Dillon when she met Ely, but she married him without divorcing her first husband. Why?

618   What famous writer penned bridge articles under the pseudonym Saxon Fairwood?

619   What convention is Dr. F. Fielding-Reid generally credited with inventing?

620   What U.S. player arrived for a World Women's Team Olympiad never having played with any of her teammates?

621   What player has had the most partners in world team competition?

622   In what state did the courts declare bridge a game of skill?

623   Who coined the term "psychic bid?"

624   What leading auction-bridge expert was slain by a still-unknown assailant in 1920?

625   What does bridge have in common with Notre Dame football?

626   By what name was Henry Jones better known?

627   What went into effect on September 1, 1962?

628   Who won the first intercollegiate tournament in 1940 — Texas, Radcliffe or Cal-Berkeley?

629   What ever happened to the "Official System?"

630   What did John Gerber do in the 1963 Bermuda Bowl that may have cost the U.S. the championship?

631   True or false? In the final of the 1937 World Championship, no U.S. player opened 1NT.

632   In 1965 *The Bridge World* magazine staged a match pitting a team of old-fashioned bidders who relied mainly on judgment against a team who used modern scientific methods. In 1990 the same type of event was staged for money in London's Portland Club. What was the outcome of both matches?

633   Why did Ely Culbertson have to avoid summoning "Al" during one period when he was editor of *The Bridge World*?

634   What 1963 gesture remains the most admirable example of international good will in bridge?

635   What was unusual about the selection of the 1961 U.S. International Team?

636   When and where was the first Swiss Teams event in ACBL tournament competition?

597   False (good grief!). Edmond Hoyle, a London barrister, lived from 1679-1769.

598   Jim Jacoby, Bobby Wolff, Bobby Goldman, Billy Eisenberg, Mike Lawrence — and Ira Corn, who filled in as the sixth until Bob Hamman could move to Dallas.

599   The bridge club where the system began was on Acol Street in London.

600   In 1972, a committee ruled a technical tie for first place (between Crane-Fisher and Granovetter-Tom) after a protest by the latter became too difficult to adjudicate.

601   A character created by the English essayist Charles Lamb to represent the ideal whist player.

602   Mahatma Gandhi.

603   "How much does it cost to destroy them?" The U.S., of course, had been clobbered by the French.

604   They defeated a "Red Team" in a trials.

605   Sabine Zenkel, in 1989, breaking Jeremy Flint's 11-week record.

606   It's a German word for an inquisitive bird of the plover family.

607   Harold Vanderbilt, the father of contract bridge.

608   Both. His father was an American engineer, working for the Russian government, who married a Russian woman. Ely was registered as an American citizen at birth.

609   True.

610   "I got up and went to work."

611   Sally Young, in 1939.

612   False. The name of the ship was the *Finland*.

613   Another name for the 4-3-2-1 count. Pitch is a card game.

614   The Robertson count.

615   The earliest documented reference to the 4-3-2-1 point count appears in a 1915 book by McCampbell. He was also one of the developers of the takeout double.

616   The negative double was called "Sputnik" because Roth and Stone introduced it in 1957, about the time the Russian satellite was orbited.

617   James Dillon committed suicide in 1919, not long after he married Josephine Murphy.

618   Alfred Sheinwold. If you know your German, the derivation will be clear.

619   The responsive double.

620   Dorothy Hayden, now Dorothy Truscott, in 1960.

621   Probably Bob Hamman, who has played with, among others, Don Krauss, Lew Mathe, Eddie Kantar, Billy Eisenberg, Mike Lawrence, Jim Jacoby and Bobby Wolff.

622   California, in a 1962 case.

623   Dorothy Rice Sims.

624   Joseph B. Elwell.

625   Both bridge and Notre Dame football had the Four Horsemen. The bridge team, which won three major events in 1932-33, consisted of P. Hal Sims, Willard Karn, David Burnstine (Bruce) and Oswald Jacoby.

626   Henry Jones (1831-1899) took the name of the London club to which he belonged — the Cavendish — and used it as a pen name in his noted works on whist.

627   The revised IMP scale that is still in use today (1990).

628   Radcliffe.

629   It slipped into oblivion when Sidney Lenz, the chief spokesman for the system, lost decisively in the famous match against the Culbertsons.

630   With the U.S. leading Italy, Gerber, the American captain, improvised a partnership between Howard Schenken and Bobby Nail. This unexpected move heartened the Italians, who believed strongly in fixed partnerships. A losing session followed for the U.S., and Italy went on to win by 19 IMPs.

631   True. The American responding methods were so poorly worked out that they were afraid to open 1NT.

632   The "Scientists" won both matches. In 1965 the "Scientists" won, although the "Traditionalists" built a large lead. In 1990 the "Scientists" won two out of three matches, but lost in total IMPs scored. As far as the inferiority or superiority of the scientific approach, these matches proved nothing.

633   Alphonse Moyse, Albert Morehead, Alfred Sheinwold and Al Sobel were on the magazine's staff simultaneously.

634   After winning a close final, the Italians presented their winners' trophies to the runner-up Americans.

635   The ACBL Board of Directors *picked* the team from among winners and runners-up in major events. The inequities in such a process are obvious. The next year, and every year until 1970, a pairs trials — not a perfect method itself — determined the team.

636   At a Cincinnati, Ohio sectional in 1967.

Construction Gang

For each of the following pairs of hands, construct an auction to
the best contract. In each problem, the exact number of bids are
given, followed by the final pass. Assume IMP scoring.

OPENER	RESPONDER
Q763	J542
Q5	AJ8
A5	KQ2
KQJ82	1073

———	———
637	638

———	———
639	640

	Pass
———	
641	

OPENER	RESPONDER
4	AJ72
Q4	K732
AQ8542	7
AJ73	K952

———	———
642	643

———	———
644	645

	Pass
———	
646	

	OPENER	RESPONDER
	K3	AJ942
	AK75	QJ106
	AK3	Q92
	Q1064	2

OPENER	RESPONDER
_____	_____
647	648
_____	_____
649	650
_____	_____
651	652
_____	_____
653	654
Pass	

	OPENER	RESPONDER
	AQ73	4
	A83	KJ74
	AQ652	K943
	3	8752

OPENER	RESPONDER
_____	_____
655	656
_____	_____
657	658
_____	_____
659	660
_____	Pass
661	

OPENER	RESPONDER
J104	Q932
AK653	2
KQ73	6
Q	KJ107652

_____   _____
662   663

_____   _____
664   665

Pass

AK764	J3
KQ4	A10853
2	J95
AJ72	Q43

_____   _____
666   667

_____   _____
668   669

_____   _____
670   671

Pass

OPENER	RESPONDER
AQ752	K83
J1064	3
AQ	KJ73
Q4	AKJ102

____	____
672	673
____	____
674	675
____	____
676	677
____	____
678	679

Pass

AKJ63	Q952
K3	A852
AJ3	8
Q108	9652

____	____
680	681
____	____
682	683

Pass

OPENER	RESPONDER
Q5	K92
AKQ1063	J2
A2	K964
Q82	10753

| _____ | _____ |
| 684 | 685 |

	Pass
_____	
686	

AJ10952	Q4
Q4	92
J103	AQ752
A8	KQJ3

| _____ | _____ |
| 687 | 688 |

| _____ | _____ |
| 689 | 690 |

| _____ | _____ |
| 691 | 692 |

	Pass
_____	
693	

OPENER	RESPONDER
A5	KQ842
KJ10642	A5
753	92
A5	KJ73

694	695

696	697

Pass

74	A82
J4	KQ1095
AKQJ3	92
A852	K103

698	699

700	701

702	703

                   Pass

704	

OPENER	RESPONDER
A5	942
AQ1064	K52
2	A9
AKQ73	J10652

_____	_____
705	706

_____	_____
707	708

_____	_____
709	710

_____	Pass
711	

OPENER	RESPONDER
A864	732
AKJ53	Q942
A6	KJ42
83	J2

_____	_____
712	713

_____	_____
714	715

Pass

OPENER	RESPONDER
AQ84	KJ753
83	92
A5	KQ73
KQ753	A2

716 _____ 717 _____

718 _____ 719 _____

720 _____ 721 _____

Pass

A5	73
Q853	AKJ72
AJ94	2
874	AKQ106

722 _____ 723 _____

724 _____ 725 _____

726 _____ 727 _____

728 _____ 729 _____

Pass

OPENER	RESPONDER
A864	Q5
5	KQ10742
AQ853	92
AJ2	843

730	731

732	733

Pass

KQ3	A965
A63	4
Q9	AK1086
AQJ53	1082

734	735

736	737

738	739

| | Pass |

| 740 | |

AQ653   K92
KQ103   85
Q53   842
2   AK875

_____   _____
741   742

_____   _____
743   744

Pass

53   AK642
AK7   3
J83   Q107
KQ653   AJ82

_____   _____
745   746

_____   _____
747   748

_____   _____
749   750

Pass

K4   AQ1062
AQ5   J963
KQ107   J3
QJ93   62

_____   _____
751   752

_____   _____
753   754

        Pass
_____
755

AQJ864   K973
AKQ   7653
A4   92
K3   J104

_____   _____
756   757

_____   _____
758   759

Pass

Q54   J93
AQ1064   K532
Q103   K52
AQ   K75

_____   _____
760   761

Pass

KQ76   A4
A8653   KQ92
K3   AJ62
AK   864

_____   _____
762   763

_____   _____
764   765

_____   _____
766   767

Pass

AK1075   J
KJ3   AQ42
3   Q82
K942   QJ763

_____   _____
768   769

_____   _____
770   771

_____   _____
772   773

_____   _____
774   775

Pass

637–641   1♣   1♠
             2♠   2NT
             3NT

642–646   1♦   1♡
             2♦   2NT
             3♣

647–654   1♣   1♠
             2NT 3♡
             4♦   4♠
             5♦   6♡

655–661   1♦   1♡
             1♠   2♦
             2♡   4♦
             5♦

Opener shows game interest despite responder's weak preference. Since responder has a maximum with all working cards, he must make a move.

662–665   1♡   1NT
             2♦   3♣

Responder should suppress his spade suit to make it easy to sign off in his seven-card suit.

666–671   1♠   1NT
             2♣   2♠
             3♡   4♡

672–679   1♠   2♣
             2♡   3♦
             3NT 4♠
             5♦   6♣

680–683   1♠   2♠
             2NT 4♠

| 684–686 | 1♡ | 1NT |
| | 3NT | |

687–693	1♠	2◇
	2♠	3♣
	3◇	3♠
	4♠	

| 694–697 | 1♡ | 1♠ |
| | 2♡ | 4♡ |

Opener's rebid promises at least six hearts.

698–704	1◇	1♡
	2♣	2♠
	3◇	3♡
	4♡	

705–711	1♡	2♡
	4♣	4◇
	4♠	6♣
	7♣	

| 712–715 | 1♡ | 2♡ |
| | 2♠ | 3♡ |

716–721	1♣	1♠
	3♠	4♣
	4◇	5♠

Without a heart control, opener must pass 5♠.

722–729	Pass	1♡
	3♡	4♣
	4◇	5♡
	5♠	7♡

| 730–733 | 1◇ | 1♡ |
| | 1♠ | 2♡ |

734–740
1♣	1◇
2NT	3♠
4♣	5♣
6♣	

In the 1977 U.S. Team Trials, an expert pair landed in 6◇, down, when opener took a 4◇ preference at his third turn.

741–744
1♠	2♣
2♡	2♠

Pairs using a forcing two–over–one style may have a hard time on this one; but did you know even Al Roth plays this non-forcing?

745–750
1♣	1♠
1NT	3♣
3♡	3NT

Opener's 3♡ shows a concentration of strength. If opener's red suits were reversed, he would bid 3◇ and might reach 6♣.

751–755
1NT	2♣
2◇	2♠
3NT	

756–759
2♣	2◇
2♠	4♠

760–761
1NT	3NT

762–767
1♡	3♡ (forcing — take credit for any forcing raise)
4NT	5♡
6♣	7♡

Opener's sequence is a variation of the grand slam force.

768–775
1♠	2♣
3♣	3♡
3♠	3NT
4♡	5♣

Bridge Movies — 2

Here are three more hands for you to bid and play. Use a piece of paper to cover the page, uncovering it as you read. When you come to a question (*italics*), decide on your answer before reading further.

I.

As South, playing in the first session of a two-session regional Master Pairs, you pick up:

KQ1064
3
A
KJ10653

Only your side is vulnerable. East, the dealer, opens 1♡. *What call do you make?* _____ 776

776   Bid 2♣. This is an example of bidding anticipation. At this vulnerability, the opponents are likely to compete — the ante may well be up to 4♡ by your next turn. It'll be easier to show both your suits if you start with clubs.

Is a 1♠ overcall so bad? _____ 777

777   It's hardly an atrocity — but if you considered making a takeout double with this pattern, don't mention it to anyone.

As it turns out, the opponents stay out of the bidding, and your partner responds 2NT. *What do you bid next?* _____ 778

778   Some players might jump to 4♠; we think 3♠ is enough. Despite the extra shape, this is a normal overcall in high cards. The spade quality is good but not spectacular.

Partner takes a preference to 4♣. *What do you call now?* _____ 779

779   Bid 4♠. At matchpoints you can't afford to miss a 5-3 spade fit. (Although North may suspect that you have five spades, he can't be sure. He may yet turn up with three-card support.) Do no more than bid 4♠; remember, East did open the bidding, and North has values in hearts. Slam chances aren't worth considering.

All pass to 4♠, and West leads the ♡4.

```
                        J93
                        K72
                        Q852
                        A72


                        KQ1064
                        3
                        A
                        KJ10653
```

WEST	NORTH	EAST	SOUTH
--	--	1♡	2♣
Pass	2NT	Pass	3♠
Pass	4♣	Pass	4♠
All Pass			

It's a good spot. Your decision to bid 2♣ worked out all right. East wins the first trick with the ♡Q and shifts to the ♠A and another spade. West follows, and you win dummy's 9. *How do you continue?* _____ 780

780   Lead the ◇Q. The contract is fairly normal, so you need to pick up the clubs to get a good matchpoint score. An expert East might refuse to cover the ◇Q, but an average East will play the king if he has it. If East fails to cover and you place the king with West, you can assign the ♣Q to East for his opening bid.

East plays the ◇K on the queen, and your ace wins. You draw the last trump — West has it. You then lead a club — 3, ace, 8. East plays the 9 on the next club lead. *Does East need the ♣Q for his opening?* _____ 781

781   No, he's already shown the ♠A, ♡AQ and ◇K — that's enough to open.

No inferences are available from the bidding. Can you draw a inference from the play? *Do you finesse or go up?* _____ 782

782   If West had a singleton club, he could have beaten you: club lead, club ruff when East won the ♠A, heart return. This would have been an easy defense, but it didn't happen — presumably because West didn't have a singleton. You should put up the ♣K.

The full deal:

```
                        J93
                        K72
                        Q852
                        A72
        875                         A2
        J954                        AQ1086
        J973                        K1064
        Q4                          98
                        KQ1064
                        3
                        A
                        KJ10653
```

What do you think of West's opening lead? _____ 783

783   With a notrump bid to his left and marked heart shortness to his right, West should have led the ♡J. This time it didn't matter. Next time it might.

II.

As South, playing in the final of the NABC IMP pairs, you hold:

```
                        92
                        KQ10642
                        A
                        Q852
```

Both sides are vulnerable. West deals and opens 1NT, 12-14 HCP. Your partner passes, and East takes out to 2♠, natural and non-forcing. *Do you bid?*

_____ 784

784   Yes. In effect, you and partner are both in the balancing position in this situation. Both West and East have limited their hand; West is about to pass 2♠. If you have a long suit — particularly hearts — you should bid. Although North is marked with some values, he may not be able to reopen comfortably without heart length.

You overcall 3♡, North raises to 4♡ and all pass. After a little thought, West leads the ◊3.

J64
A9
J7542
A94

92
KQ10642
A
Q852

WEST	NORTH	EAST	SOUTH
1NT	Pass	2♠	3♡
Pass	4♡	All Pass	

Uh oh! You and partner were operating on different planes in the bidding. (You can discuss this situation later, but for now do not scowl at dummy or make trenchant comments on the adequacy of the contract — that will encourage the defenders.) *What play do you have for 4♡?* _____ 785

785   Since two spade losers are inevitable, you must pick up the trumps and play the clubs for one loser. The obvious chance in clubs is K-x-x with East.

Where are the spade honors? _____ 786

786   East has at least one and surely has the king, since West would have led a spade from A-K-x or K-Q-x.

Where are the diamond honors? _____ 787

787   They're probably split. East has at least one, since West wouldn't lead low from K-Q-x-x.

Who has the ♣K? _____ 788

788   West. The defenders have 19 high-card points, and East has at least 5 points in diamonds and spades. West must hold the ♣K to have his bid. *Can you play clubs for one loser if West has the king?* _____ 789

789   Maybe. If West has K-x, you can lead low to the 9, losing to East. But West's king will pop up on the next lead, letting you win dummy's ace and finesse the ♣8.

How many spades does West have? _____ 790

790   No more than three; probably exactly three.

How many diamonds? _____ 791

791   Three or, more likely, four.

If West has two clubs, as you hope, how many hearts will he have?

_____ 792

792   No fewer than four.

How do you play? _____ 793

793   Win the ♢A and lead a heart to the 9. When it holds, cash the ♡A. When East discards a spade, you can ruff a diamond, draw trumps and lead a club to the 9. The full deal (top of next page):

```
                        J64
                        A9
                        J7542
                        A94
        AQ7                          K10853
        J873                         5
        K1083                        Q96
        K7                           J1063
                        92
                        KQ10642
                        A
                        Q852
```

Could West have made it harder on you? _____ 794

794   Yes, if he puts up his king on the first club lead. As the cards lie, you
       can take the ace and return a low club, winning the 8 if East doesn't
       split. But if West's second club were the 10 or jack, you would either
       have to let the king hold or win and return a club to the *queen*.

III.

As South, playing in the Unit qualifying stage of the North American
Pairs, you hold:

74
AK953
4
KQ1053

Neither side is vulnerable. North deals and open 1◊. The opponents pass
throughout. You respond 1♡, and partner raises to 2♡. *How do you continue?*
_____ 795

795   Since a suitable minimum (Axx, Qxxx, Q10xx, Ax) from North makes
       6♡ a good shot, you must at least make a try for slam. Jump to 4♣,
       suggesting a big heart-club two-suiter. North should realize you are
       interested in slam (since 4♣ commits you to game) and he should pay
       attention to his club fit, trump quality and side aces.

Many players would try 3♣, an inferior bid because it leaves partner temporarily in the dark about your intentions. Note that 4♣ is valuable here as a natural bid. It could also be used as a splinter, if agreed by the partnership. It probably should not be used as Gerber, which normally applies only when the first or last bid was notrump.

Over your 4♣, North cubids 4♠. What call do you make? _____ 796

796   Bid 6♡. North obviously lacks the ◇A, which may be *good* news. You would like it if most of his values were in the other suits. Presumably, North's hand is no worse than the "suitable minimum" shown above. If he has only the ♣A and decent trumps, you'll have a play for slam.

All pass, and West leads the ♠Q.

> A63
> J42
> KQ852
> A9
>
>
> 74
> AK953
> 4
> KQ1053

What's your opinion of North's bidding? _____ 797

797   Ours is unprintable. Once North raises hearts on J-x-x, it's questionable whether he should cuebid *below* game, much less go past game to show the ♠A. Opposite a heart-club hand, his diamond honors are too likely to be wasted.

Does 6♡ have a play? _____ 798

798   Oh, 6♡ has a *wonderful* play. To start, win the ♠A and lead a trump to clarify the trump position. East plays the 10, and your king wins. *What next?* _____ 799

799   The only chance is that the ♡Q is about to fall from East. Even then, you must bring in the clubs, and you'll need West, who will hold the last trump, to hold four. If you can run four club tricks and pitch two spades from dummy while West follows, you can ruff your spade loser with dummy's jack and lose only the ◊A.

You should lead a club to the 9 now, since West is twice as likely to have the ♣J if he has four clubs. If you cash the ♡A first, you can't get off dummy after making your club play.

After you win the ♣9 and cash the ace, lead a second heart. Lo and behold, the queen falls from East. Your 4.8% ship has come in! The full deal:

```
                    A63
                    J42
                    KQ852
                    A9
      QJ102                       K985
      876                         Q10
      97                          AJ1063
      J862                        74
                    74
                    AK953
                    4
                    KQ1053
```

What would you have done if East had followed low on the first heart?

_____ 800

800   You'd finesse the 9. If East had Q-10-x (a 17% chance), you draw another trump, lead a club to the ace and try a club to the 10, making the necessary assumption that *East* has four clubs.

Just for Fun

801 If you deal out a brand new pack without shuffling it, what will your hand be?

802 What card is known as the Devil's Bedposts?

803 If you hold 17 high-card points, how many controls (A=2, K=1) will you have most often?

804 What's a "Josephine?"

805 Who was William M. Anderson?

806 Remember the TV show "Championship Bridge with Charles Goren?" Who was the announcer and co-host? Who was the sponsor?

807 What was the original version of the SOS redouble called?

808 Where did the Astro convention gets its name?

809 You probably know the Rabbi's Rule — "When the king is singleton, play the ace." Was there a real Rabbi?

810 How many players did the U.S. use in the 1951 Bermuda Bowl?

811 What was the takeout double originally called?

812 Name four players with last names beginning with the letter "Z" who have won national titles.

813 What two well-known bridge players have fathers who won Nobel Prizes?

814 What noted bridge personality played bridge with Hugh Hefner and participated in the founding of *Playboy*? What player was asked to pose for the magazine?

815 Who is the only graduate of Vanderbilt University to have won the Vanderbilt Knockout Teams?

816   What leading East Coast player has three double letters in his last name?

817   What bridge champion also held records at bowling, was expert at magic and table tennis, and shot his age at golf at 69?

818   Who invented the *lebensohl* convention?

819   True or false? Alvin Roth devised the negative double during a flight to Europe for a high-stakes rubber-bridge game.

820   True or false? The maneuver in which a defender sacrifices a high card to dislodge an entry is the "Merrimack Coup."

821   What's the difference between the play described in Question 820 and the "Deschapelles Coup?"

822   What were the stakes in the 1970 rubber bridge match between Jeremy Flint-Jonathan Cansino and the Omar Sharif Bridge Circus?

823   Once in about how many sessions would you expect to hold all four aces?

824   Which pair has represented their country in the World Team Olympiad the most times?

825   What name did the "Coup Without a Name" eventually get?

826   What bridge great died in 1949 while bidding a hand at the Havana Country Club?

827   What noted composer and concert pianist is the son of a famous bridge player?

828   The Rule of 11 applies when a lead is fourth best. What's the rule when the lead is third best?

829   What's the most likely distribution of a 13-card hand?

830   By what name was the Blackwood convention originally known —
      (A) Redwood, (B) Wormwood, or (C) Hardwood?

831 What's the historical significance of this club holding — AQ in dummy opposite J98632?

832 What's the Rush-Bagot Convention?

833 Oswald Jacoby probably could have been as great at chess as he was at bridge. Why did he give up the game?

834 By what name did Helen Martin become better known?

835 Who was on deck when Bobby Thompson hit "the shot heard round the world" to win the 1951 National League pennant? (Oops, wrong game.)

836 What "Quiz Kid" of radio fame became the ACBL's youngest Life Master in 1952?

837 Your partner leads a suit in which both you and declarer are void. You ruff with the trump queen, declarer overruffs with the king and now partner's J-x is worth a trick. What is this defensive maneuver called?

838 What are Pearson Points?

839 What is the Vondracek Phenomenon?

840 What are the odds against being dealt a yarborough (no card above a 9)?

801 When we tried it, we got ♠AK95 ♡Q84 ◇Q84 ♣J73.

802 The ♣4.

803 Six.

804 The Grand Slam Force, as it is widely known in Europe. Ely Culbertson developed the convention, but his wife Josephine wrote it up.

805 He was a Toronto actuary who developed the 4-3-2-1 count and offered it to Charles Goren.

806 Alex Dreier; North American Van Lines.

807 The Kock-Werner redouble, after the Swedish pair who invented it.

808 The name comes from the first letters of the names of the players who devised the convention: Paul Allinger, Roger Stern and Larry Rosler.

809 The *Encyclopedia of Bridge* attributes the Rabbi's Rule to Milton Shattner, a New York attorney nicknamed "The Rabbi" because of his authoritative pronouncements of this and other convictions governing his play.

810 Six. Actually, the team had only five players, but Julius Rosenblum, the non-playing captain, sat in for a few deals toward the end of the match.

811 Until about 1930, it was called the negative double.

812 John Zilic, Ray Zoller, Jim Zimmerman and Mahmood Zia (in Pakistan, first and last names are interchangeable).

813 Milton Friedman (Economics) is Jan Friedman Martel's father; Hans Bethe (Physics) is Henry Bethe's father.

814 Max Hardy and Rhoda Walsh (not vice-versa).

815 Tom Sanders.

816 Mike Cappelletti.

817   Sidney Lenz.

818   We know who didn't invent it — Ken Lebensold, who has disclaimed authorship of the convention. Lebensohl was first written up by August Boehm.

819   False. Roth says the story is untrue.

820   False. The ship was the coalship *Merrimac*, which was scuttled during the Spanish-American War. The Civil War ironclad that fought the *Monitor* was the *Merrimack*.

821   In the Deschapelles Coup a defender sacrifices a high card to force an entry to his *partner's* hand.

822   An English pound a point — at that time, about $2.40 a point.

823   14.

824   Probably Eric Murray-Sami Kehela, who have played for Canada in every Olympiad except 1984.

825   The Scissors Coup.

826   P. Hal Sims.

827   Easley Blackwood Jr.

828   The Rule of 12.

829   Any 4-4-3-2.

830   (B) Wormwood. Blackwood disguised his convention because he wasn't sure how his employer, the Metropolitan Life Insurance company, would react to his association with a card game.

831   This was the trump suit on the famous deal from the 1975 Bermuda Bowl, in which Belladonna-Garozzo reached 7♣ for Italy — making 7 because Eddie Kantar held the K-10 of trumps onside.

832   If you got this one right, we give up. The Rush-Bagot Convention is the treaty between the U.S and Canada to maintain an unfortified border.

833   Jacoby said chess was too slow for him. No matter what the game, he always hated waiting for an opponent to make a move.

834   Helen Martin was the maiden name of Helen Sobel.

835   Oh, what the heck. It was Willie Mays.

836   Richard Freeman.

837   An uppercut. If you said trump promotion, you made a common error. In a trump promotion, declarer must either ruff low and be overruffed or ruff high at the cost of establishing a trump trick for the defense.

838   In fourth seat, count Pearson Points by adding high-card points to the number of spades. With 14 or more, according to Mr. Pearson (we've seen it spelled "Pierson"), you open the bidding.

839   The condition in which the weaker of two combined holdings may prove more effective as a trump suit. The Vondracek Phenomenon was first discussed in an article in *The Bridge World*.

840   1827 to 1. The Duke of Yarborough, it is said, would offer to bet a pound, giving 1000 to 1 odds, that a player would not hold such a hand. It was a good bet.

QUICK QUIZ

First Letters Only

Can you figure out the bridge aphorisms that these letters represent? (For example, "N _ _ _ _   l _ _ _   f _ _ _   a k _ _ _" would be "Never lead from a king.") Some of these are common expressions; some are cliche's and some are sound bridge advice. Solving all 20 would be remarkable.

841   E _ _ _ _   e _ _ _,   n _ _ _   n _ _ _ _.

842   F _ _ _ _ _ _   f _ _ _   y _ _ _   l _ _ _ _ _ _   and s _ _ _ _ _ _ _ _.

843   C _ _ _ _ _   y _ _ _   w _ _ _ _ _ _ _   i_   n _ _ _ _ _ _;   c _ _ _ _   y _ _ _   l _ _ _ _ _   i_   s _ _ _   c _ _ _ _ _ _ _ _.

844   L _ _ _   t _ _ _ _ _ _   s _ _ _ _ _ _ _   and u _   t _   w _ _ _ _ _ _ _.

845   K _ _ _   w _ _ _ _ _ _ _,   t _ _ _ _   l _ _ _ _ _ _.

846   N _ _   t _ _ _ _ _ _ _   t _ _   i _ _ _   d _ _ _!

847   N _ _ _ _   u _ _ _ _ _ _ _ _   a _   a _ _.

848   R _ _ _ _ _ _   y _ _ _   p _ _ _ _ _ _ _'_   l _ _ _.

849   A _ _ _   w _ _ _   m _ _ _ _   t_   t _ _ _   k _ _ _ _.

850   W _ _ _   i_   d _ _ _ _   l _ _ _   t _ _ _ _ _.

851 S_ _ _ _ _ h_ _ _ l_ _.

852 F_ _ _ _ d_ _ _ _ _ _ _, n_ _ d_ _ _ _.

853 W_ _ _ t_ _ l_ _ s_ _ _ _, b_ _ t_ _ h_ _ _ _ _,
r_ _ _ _ _ _ f_ _ _ _.

854 T_ _ q_ _ _ _ l_ _ _ o_ _ t_ _ j_ _ _.

855 C_ _ _ _ a_ h_ _ _ _ w_ _ _ a_ h_ _ _ _.

856 O_ _ p_ _ _ i_ w_ _ _ _ t_ _ f_ _ _ _ _ _ _.

857 D_ _'_ s_ _ _ a b_ _ t_ d_ a m_ _'_ j_ _.

858 G_ _ t_ _ k_ _ _ _ _ _ o_ _ t_ _ s_ _ _ _ _.

859 N_ d_ _ _ _ _, n_ t_ _ _ _ _ _.

860 N_ _ _ _ g_ _ _ a r_ _ _ a_ _ a s_ _ _ _.

841   Eight ever, nine never.

842   Fourth from your longest and strongest.

843   Count your winners in notrump; count your losers in suit contracts.

844   Lead through strength and up to weakness.

845   Keep winners, throw losers.

846   Not through the iron duke!

847   Never underlead an ace.

848   Return your partner's lead!

849   Aces were meant to take kings.

850   When in doubt, lead trumps.

851   Second hand low.

852   Force declarer, not dummy.

853   With two long suits, bid the higher-ranking first.

854   The queen lies over the jack.

855   Cover an honor with an honor.

856   One peek is worth two finesses.

857   Don't send a boy to do a man's job.

858   Get the kiddies off the street.

859   No double, no trouble.

860   Never give a ruff and a sluff.

Whose Fault? — Constructive Bidding

You'll be shown an auction and the opening and responding hands. Decide who was more to blame for reaching an inaccurate contract. Write an "O" for opener, an "R" for responder.

OPENER	RESPONDER	OPENER	RESPONDER
K104	AQ863	AK54	Q10763
KQ3	754	8	752
4	J53	AQ54	K63
AKQ1052	43	AQ87	K3

OPENER	RESPONDER	OPENER	RESPONDER
1♣	1♠	1♣	1♠
3♣	Pass	4♠	Pass

4♠ would have made five.
Whose fault? _____ 861

Whose fault? _____ 862

OPENER	RESPONDER	OPENER	RESPONDER
K54	AQJ10	K4	AQ76
J2	A953	A108653	KQJ2
Q92	65	K	76
AKJ82	Q54	A1052	Q43

OPENER	RESPONDER	OPENER	RESPONDER
1♣	1♡	1♡	3♡ [1]
1NT	3NT	4♣	4♠
Pass		5♢	6♡
		Pass	

The defense cashed five diamond tricks. 4♠ makes four. (Declarer discards a heart if the defenders lead three rounds of diamonds.)
Whose fault? _____ 863

[1] Forcing

6♡ is a poor contract.
Whose fault? _____ 864

OPENER	RESPONDER
K8	A5
3	K1064
AKJ842	65
AQ52	K10963
1◇	1♡
3◇	3NT
Pass	

3NT made, but so would have 6♣. Whose fault? _____ 865

OPENER	RESPONDER
A105	KQ763
A82	7653
AKJ3	Q52
1042	7
1NT	2♣
2◇	2♠
3♠	Pass

Whose fault? _____ 866

OPENER	RESPONDER
AK4	QJ952
K853	A7
K4	Q753
AKJ4	32
2NT	3♣
3♡	3♠
4♠	Pass

Whose fault? _____ 867

OPENER	RESPONDER
AQ953	J104
K1064	AQ3
3	KJ2
A76	KJ103
1♠	2NT
3♡	3NT
Pass	

The opening lead was a diamond from A-10-x-x-x-x. The spade finesse lost, and a diamond return gave the defense five more tricks. 4♠ would have made. Whose fault? _____ 868

OPENER	RESPONDER		OPENER	RESPONDER
AK1064	Q3		Q3	A1054
AK	Q542		AK432	76
Q9	10832		K32	A7
QJ104	K92		QJ3	AK1095
1♠	1NT		1♡	1♠
3♣	3♠		1NT	3♣
4♠	Pass		3NT	Pass

The ♠J didn't fall, so 4♠ went down. 3NT is better. Whose fault? _____ 869

3NT made, but the excellent club slam was missed. Whose fault? _____ 870

OPENER	RESPONDER		OPENER	RESPONDER
Q10	AKJ63		KQ4	AJ732
K653	A4		A53	KQ102
AQ64	KJ103		J1054	AK
K104	52		A64	52
1◇	1♠		1◇	1♠
1NT	3◇		1NT	3♡
3NT	Pass		3♠	4♠
			Pass	

Who was at fault for missing the laydown 6◇? _____ 871

Whose fault? _____ 872

OPENER	RESPONDER		OPENER	RESPONDER
AKJ864	3		76	K10543
AQJ4	K10532		AQ	953
AK	J42		AQ953	J10
4	Q732		AJ53	KQ2
2♣	2◇		1◇	1♠
2♠	2NT		2♣	Pass
3♡	4♡			
Pass				

Whose fault? _____ 873

3NT from opener's side was unbeatable. Whose fault? _____ 874

OPENER	RESPONDER
5	432
J32	AKQ4
AKQ104	853
AK105	432
1♢	1♡
2♣	2♢
2♡	Pass

5♢ was almost cold, and 6♡ might make! Whose fault for not reaching game? ____ 875

OPENER	RESPONDER
AQ6	107542
54	AK9
A954	32
KJ72	A85
1♢	1♠
2♣	2NT
Pass	

2NT made, but 10 tricks were available at spades. Whose fault? ____ 876

OPENER	RESPONDER
—	KQJ10853
QJ107543	—
Q532	AK
76	AQ83
3♡	3NT
4♡	Pass

Whose fault? ____ 877

OPENER	RESPONDER
AK6	QJ75
KQ42	A85
AQ63	KJ52
Q3	86
1♢	1♠
2NT	3♢
3♠	3NT
Pass	

Whose fault? ____ 878

OPENER	RESPONDER
QJ65	K3
K3	AQ4
Q7	AKJ32
AKJ43	862
1♣	1♢
1♠	3NT
Pass	

Whose fault? ____ 879

OPENER	RESPONDER
AQ653	J4
3	AQJ62
653	AK2
AKJ3	Q106
1♠	2♡
3♣	4NT
5♡	6NT
Pass	

Whose fault? ____ 880

OPENER	RESPONDER
53	KQ4
AKJ53	62
J53	104
K104	AQJ732

1♡	2♣
2♡	2♠
3♣	4♣
5♣	Pass

Whose fault? _____ 881

OPENER	RESPONDER
Q63	--
AK852	Q9643
103	AQJ62
AQ4	863

1♡	4♡
Pass	

The diamond finesse lost, but 12 tricks were there. Whose fault? _____ 883

OPENER	RESPONDER
K1083	AQ762
A742	K3
AQ10	K9
85	AJ42

1♢	1♠
2♠	3♣
3♡	4♢
4♠	5♡
5♠	Pass

Whose fault? _____ 885

OPENER	RESPONDER
76	1054
KJ3	AQ952
8542	A7
AK43	Q65

Pass	1♡
2♣	Pass

4♡ was a good spot. Whose fault? _____ 882

OPENER	RESPONDER
AK542	3
Q82	A65
AJ6	73
KJ	Q965432

1♠	1NT
2NT	3♣
3NT	Pass

Declarer was favored with a heart opening lead from the king, but 3NT went down when clubs divided 3-1. Whose fault? _____ 884

861   Opener. His hand was too promising for a 3♣ rebid. It's better to improvise a reverse to 2♡, forcing. Responder would rebid 2♠, which opener could raise. 2♡ is not dangerous — if responder raises hearts viciously, presumably with four-card support, he must have five or more spades. He would respond 1♡ with 4-4 in the majors.

862   Opener. His 4♠ rebid suggested a balanced hand. Opener should instead bid diamonds, then jump in spades. This allows responder to judge that he has three working cards and a "valuable" heart holding.

863   Responder. He should have responded 1♠, treating his suit like a five-carder. The superior spade game would then be reached.

864   Responder. With two queens on the side and a wasted jack in trumps, his hand was not the stuff that slams are made of. The 4♠ cuebid (going past game) was questionable, and the jump to 6♡ was a repeat of the same values.

865   Opener. 2♣ was a more flexible rebid than 3◇. The auction might have been: 1◇-1♡, 2♣-3♣, 3◇-3♠, 4♠-6♣.

866   Opener should bid 3◇ over 2♠, showing concentrated side strength. Responder, with a diamond fit, would jump to 4♠.

867   Opener, with a good spade fit and a maximum with prime cards, should make an advance cuebid of 4♣ over 3♠. When responder answers with 4♡, opener can drive to 6♠.

868   Responder sank the ship when he declined to take a 3♠ preference over 3♡. The 3NT bid was the worst sort of masterminding.

869   Opener, knowing responder probably has only a doubleton spade, should bid 3NT over 3♠, offering a choice of games and suggesting 5-2-2-4 distribution.

870   Responder misrepresented his suit lengths. He should respond 2♣ to 1♡, planning to bid spades next. A possible sequence: 1♡-2♣, 3♣-3♠, 3NT-4♣, 4♡-6♣. The actual bidding offered no hope of reaching slam.

871   Responder. He should have jumped to 2♠ over 1◇, showing slam potential immediately. As it was, opener had no idea that slam was in the picture and couldn't cooperate.

872   Opener. He should have jumped to 4♠ over 3♡. Responder, reassured about trump quality, would make a slam try that opener could accept.

873   Responder failed to appreciate the power of his hand — he should bid at least 5♡ over 3♡. Since opener's 3♡ bid was forcing, responder could have had nothing for his raise to 4♡.

874   Responder should take a false preference to 2◇, giving opener another chance in case he has extra strength or distribution. Opener would try 2NT, which responder should raise to 3NT.

875   Responder. Opener's sequence promised better than minimum strength, since he could have raised to 2♡ directly, but chose to make three bids instead. Responder might have jumped to 4♡ over 2♡; he at least should bid 3♡.

876   Opener's sequence hardly described his hand — he should raise 1♠ to 2♠. Responder has an easy lift to 4♠. (Also, we suggest a 1♣ opening.)

877   Opener should pass 3NT. Once he preempts, responder makes the decisions. Responder did well to bid 3NT, the only sure game.

878   This is a famous U.S. disaster from the 1958 Bermuda Bowl. No doubt opener, who jumped to 2NT without a club stopper and then heard responder suggest doubt about notrump, should run from 3NT.

879   Another case where failure to jump shift was costly. Responder should bid 2◇ over 1♣, planning to bid notrump next. Opener would then drive to slam. Alternatively, if the partnership plays a second-round jump to 2NT as forcing, responder's 3NT would signify 16-17 points and opener would move.

880   Opener. He should have had more for his 3♣ bid. Responder's slam bid opposite a reverse looks reasonable to us.

881   Opener. He mistakenly thought he had to bid over 4♣. The lesson here is that *game-forcing* auctions shouldn't be forcing to 11-trick contracts (minor-suit games).

882   Opener (the dealer) was wrong to temporize with 2♣ as a passed hand, risking a pass from partner. A jump to 3♡ is better, but 3♣, suggesting a heart fit and club values, is best and might let partner bid game. (Some partnerships might handle this deal successfully with the Drury convention.)

883   Responder. With two side first-round controls and a source of tricks, his hand had far too much slam potential for the preemptive 4♡ bid. We'd rather jump to 3◇ than bid 4♡!

884   Opener bid over a signoff and got what he deserved. Of course, 3NT might have made — then opener would compliment himself on an astute bid and go merrily breaking discipline again on the next deal.

885   From the 1969 Bermuda Bowl. The rot set in when opener chose the devious 3♡ bid instead of a straightforward 4♠, so we think he gets most of the blame.

Whose Fault? — Competitive Misadventures

You'll be shown a competitive auction and the East-West hands. Decide who was more to blame for the poor result, West or East. Neither side is vulnerable throughout, matchpoints.

KJ108653	A2
J62	4
4	KQ962
82	AKJ65

WEST	NORTH	EAST	SOUTH
--	--	--	2♡
3♠	Pass	4NT	Pass
5♣	Pass	5♠	All Pass

The defense cashed a heart and the ◊ A, then forced dummy to ruff a heart. North's Q-x-x of trumps was worth a trick — down one. Whose fault for getting too high? _____ 886

A764	83
KQ83	AJ65
AQ3	J954
65	1043

WEST	NORTH	EAST	SOUTH
--	--	--	1♣
Dbl	1♠	All Pass	

1♠ made two, and East-West could have taken nine tricks in hearts. Whose fault? _____ 887

```
KJ2              Q5
AJ2              76
AK4              9653
J103             KQ954
```

WEST	NORTH	EAST	SOUTH
1NT	2♡	2NT	Pass
3NT	All Pass		

North led the ♡10 to the king and ace. West tried a club, but North took the ace, cashed the ♡Q and led another heart. Since North also had the ♠A, the best West could do was cash eight tricks for down one. Whose fault? _____ 888

```
--               KJ3
KQJ9753          A6
Q73              A105
1053             J9842
```

WEST	NORTH	EAST	SOUTH
3♡	3♠	4♡	4♠
5♡	Dbl	All Pass	

5♡ went down two, and 4♠ would also have gone down two. Whose fault? _____ 889

```
J43              92
10653            KQJ4
Q6               K832
AKQ4             1032
```

WEST	NORTH	EAST	SOUTH
1♣	Pass	1♡	1♠
Pass	2♠	All Pass	

2♠ made two, and East-West could have taken nine tricks in hearts. Whose fault? _____ 890

K1043		A962	
76		KQJ4	
AQJ5		763	
K104		J7	

WEST	NORTH	EAST	SOUTH
1◊	Pass	1♡	2♣
Pass	Pass	2◊	All Pass

West scraped home in 2◊, losing a spade, a heart, two
diamonds and a club. Did anyone miss the boat? _____ 891

A104		87	
653		AKQ92	
KQ105		J32	
A65		Q43	

WEST	NORTH	EAST	SOUTH
1◊	Pass	1♡	1♠
1NT	Pass	3NT	All Pass

Hearts split, but since South had five spades and the ◊A,
the contract had no chance. Whose fault? _____ 892

A1093		Q864	
43		76	
KJ54		A732	
A65		K42	

WEST	NORTH	EAST	SOUTH
--	--	--	1♡
Dbl	Pass	2♠	3♡
3♠	All Pass		

South held KJ2, AKQ952, 108, Q7, so both 3♡ and 3♠
would fail. Did either East or West do something wrong?
_____ 893

A62
KQ65
A953
64

K108
J102
K842
KJ5

WEST	NORTH	EAST	SOUTH
1◇	2♣	2NT	All Pass

The opening lead was a club, won by North's ace. East won the club continuation with the jack, lost to the ♡A and had two spade tricks, three hearts, two diamonds and two clubs. Whose fault for missing the 24-pt game? _____ 894

K63
AKJ2
J2
QJ106

AQ82
Q753
65
K92

WEST	NORTH	EAST	SOUTH
—	—	—	1◇
Dbl	3◇	4♠	All Pass

4♠ went down when North turned up with a trump trick. What went wrong? _____ 895

6
AK965
KJ53
Q76

Q53
QJ42
42
A952

WEST	NORTH	EAST	SOUTH
1♡	1♠	2♡	2♠
3♡	Pass	4♡	All Pass

Although declarer guessed diamonds, he lost a diamond, a spade and two clubs (North held K-J-10) — down one. Whose fault? _____ 896

76		K53	
AK753		10842	
K65		94	
K74		A1065	

WEST	NORTH	EAST	SOUTH
1♡	1♠	2♡	2♠
All Pass			

North brought home 2♠, losing a spade, a heart, a diamond and two clubs. East-West could have made 3♡, losing a trick in each suit. Whose fault? _____ 897

AK763		52	
9		KJ1085	
AQ9		43	
Q1053		J984	

WEST	NORTH	EAST	SOUTH
1♠	2♡	Dbl (Penalty)	3♢
Dbl	All Pass		

South, who held J4, 2, KJ108652, A72, lost two spades and two diamonds, making the contract. Whose fault? _____ 898

763		--	
K8652		AQ43	
J		K854	
Q953		AKJ102	

WEST	NORTH	EAST	SOUTH
--	4♠	Dbl	Pass
Pass	Pass		

North, who had 8-1-3-1 distribution, took eight spade tricks and two diamonds to make his contract. Meanwhile, East-West could have made 6♣ or 6♡. Whose fault? _____ 899

Q93
AQ965
7
KQ76

10862
K103
AQ32
83

WEST	NORTH	EAST	SOUTH
1♡	2◇	Pass	Pass
Dbl	All Pass		

North made the contract. Whose fault? _____ 900

K10753
87
Q76
K83

AQ4
J92
AK83
J54

WEST	NORTH	EAST	SOUTH
—	1♡	Pass	Pass
1♠	Pass	4♠	All Pass

Since the diamonds failed to split and the clubs lay poorly, West took only eight tricks. Whose fault? _____ 901

Q953
Q104
A3
K964

AJ1064
52
Q842
53

WEST	NORTH	EAST	SOUTH
—	1♡	Pass	2♡
Pass	Pass	2♠	Pass
Pass	3♡	Pass	Pass
3♠	All Pass		

North held K2, A9863, K1075, AJ. East was down one in 3♠, losing two hearts, a diamond and two clubs. 3♡ would have gone down one, off two spades, two diamonds and a heart. Whose fault? _____ 902

J862		A43	
Q87		KJ1065	
85		76	
K962		AQ7	

WEST	NORTH	EAST	SOUTH
—	1◇	Dbl	2◇
2♠	All Pass		

The defenders got three trump tricks, two diamonds and the ♡A, defeating the contract. Did anyone err? _____ 903

J72		AK853	
762		—	
J72		Q103	
A1052		KQJ63	

WEST	NORTH	EAST	SOUTH
—	1♡	1♠	4♡
Pass	Pass	5♣	All Pass

Declarer lost a spade and two diamonds — the same tricks he would have lost in 4♠. (4♡ makes four.) Whose fault? _____ 904

A942		J53	
K43		852	
A64		K73	
K102		AQ73	

WEST	NORTH	EAST	SOUTH
—	—	—	1♡
Dbl	Pass	3♣	Pass
3NT	All Pass		

After a heart lead to the ace and a heart return, West could take only eight tricks. Whose fault? _____ 905

J108642
74
Q9
AJ2

K93
AJ53
73
KQ76

WEST	NORTH	EAST	SOUTH
—	3◊	Pass	Pass
3♠	Pass	4♠	Dbl
All Pass			

West lost two diamonds, two spades and a heart for -300.
Whose fault? _____ 906

K7
AKJ963
AQJ3
4

Q652
Q84
982
K73

WEST	NORTH	EAST	SOUTH
1♡	2♣	2♡	3♣
4♡	5♣	Pass	Pass
5♡	All Pass		

North's hand was A4, 5, K654, Q108652. 5♣ would have
gone down at least two tricks. In 5♡, West lost the ◊K and
the two black aces. Whose fault? _____ 907

76
AQ65
AKJ63
K4

J54
KJ943
75
Q62

WEST	NORTH	EAST	SOUTH
1◊	Pass	1♡	2♠
3♡	All Pass		

East took 10 tricks. Whose fault? _____ 908

K9   Q1043
AJ3   76
KQ1083   964
AQ5   K742

WEST	NORTH	EAST	SOUTH
—	—	—	2♡
Dbl	Pass	2♠	Pass
2NT	All Pass		

Since South had the ♡KQ as expected, the defense got
only one heart trick and two aces. Whose fault for missing
game? _____ 909

KJ108   Q976
A73   J842
96432   7
4   AQ92

WEST	NORTH	EAST	SOUTH
—	—	—	1◇
1♠	Dbl (negative)	Redbl	Pass
Pass	2♣	3♠	Pass
Pass	Dbl	All Pass	

A trump lead held West to seven tricks: three spades in
hand, one ruff in dummy, two side aces and an extra heart.
Whose fault for -300? _____ 910

886   West. East had his bids. When South preempts, a jump overcall by West is a strong action, not another preempt.

887   East should compete with 2♡ over 1♠. It's easier if East imagines that West has *bid* hearts, and East has enough to *raise*.

888   West. East's 2NT is competitive, not invitational. Even with a maximum, West cannot go on to game. With a sound invitation, East must bid game himself.

889   West. Once he preempts, he should let East make the partnership's decisions.

890   West. Despite his dead-minimum opening bid, he can't afford to suppress his heart support.

891   East should reopen with a double (cooperative, since he sits under the club bidder). If West passes, the defense collects 300. If West bids 2♠, he probably goes +140.

892   West. To bid 1NT freely over 1♠, he needs extra strength. East's 3NT raise was a good bid that would have worked if West had held the ♠J instead of the 10.

893   Not really. West, despite the four-card trump support, might have passed 3♡, and East would then judge to defend with his flat minimum. Still, it could easily have been right for him to compete to 3♠, since South was a favorite to hold the ◊Q.

894   East. After North's overcall, East should promote his club holding and jump to 3NT.

895   East surely should cuebid 4◊ over 3◊, letting West pick a major suit.

896   East. West's 3♡ is strictly competitive — he can bid three of a minor to try for game. Even with a maximum raise (which the East hand was not, since the ♠Q was wasted), East shouldn't bid 4♡.

897   East, who holds four trumps, a working ♠K and a side ace, should compete to 3♡ over 2♠.

898   East. His double of 2♡, with a trump stack but no high-card strength, was shortsighted and induced West's unsuccessful double of 3◊. Perhaps this is one extra reason to play negative doubles — it prevents players from making bad penalty doubles.

899   East. He could have bid 4NT for takeout. The popular meaning of the double is high-card values but no particular support for hearts or clubs. Therefore, it would have been speculative for West to run out.

   Some partnerships treat the double of 4♠ for takeout (Al Roth, for one, recommends it). However, without a firm agreement, it is best to play safe. In this instance, a 4NT bid was less likely to cause a disastrous misunderstanding.

900   East was wrong to convert the double. He had undisclosed heart support and no diamond intermediates. He should have raised to 2♡ directly.

901   West's balancing overcall was fine. East got carried away with his 15 points and ignored his handfull of losers. A 2♡ cuebid, planning to pass a 2♠ rebid by West, would have been enough.

902   West should have passed 3♡. East's risky balance improved East-West's chance to go plus. West punished partner for his enterprise.

903   East got what he deserved — a missed 5-3 heart fit — by doubling 1◊ instead of overcalling 1♡ on his 13-point hand.

904   East should probably anticipate the competition and start with 2♣. He could then bid 4♠ over 4♡ and play in the best contract. A Michaels cuebid would also have worked, if East returned to the auction at the four level with 4♠ or a double (West converts to 4♠).

905   East should prefer a conservative 2♣ response. A jump response in a *minor* suggests a longer suit. West will seldom want to bid an 11-trick minor-suit game, but will often want to try 3NT if East has a source of tricks. If East had produced a fifth club, West would have made 3NT.

906   We think West should pass 3♦. We're all for balancing, but you must draw the line somewhere. If East has enough for West to make 3♠, East will bid at least 4♠.

907   East, although, on a high level, West might also be at fault. Since East has a poor raise and his ♣K is better for defense, he should probably try for a plus score by doubling 5♣. However, some would say that West did not create a forcing situation by jumping to 4♡; if West wanted East's opinion at the five level, he would have cuebid 4♣ on the way to game, promising high-card values. Then if the opponents bid 5♣, East would know whose hand it was and would *surely* double to stop West from bidding on.

908   West must let the preempt push him around a bit. To avoid being shut out, West would bid 3♡ with any sound minimum. With his actual hand — a sound game invitation — West must jump to 4♡.

909   Although West showed at least 18 points with his double followed by 2NT, East's pass could have been right. We think West should bid 3NT over 2♠, taking the pressure off his partner. After the preempt, West must bid on the assumption that East has a few values. Furthermore, West's ♡J is promoted.

910   West overcalled because he *thought* East would be short in diamonds and thus would produce spade support. East, however, bid his side of the table, not knowing he was *expected* to hold four trumps and a singleton — he did well to bid only 3♠. West is the culprit for too much masterminding.

Incidentally, the trump lead was indicated because East-West were known to be bidding on distribution rather than high-cards.

QUICK QUIZ

Systems Around the World — 2

Match the following noted partnerships with their bidding systems.

911	Munir Ata-Ullah/Jan-E-Alam Fazli	Big Club (nonvul.); East. Sci. (vul.)
912	Pierre Ghestem-Rene Bacherich	Two-Over-One Game Force
913	Mario Franco-Michele Giovine	Colonial Acol
914	John Lowenthal-Paul Heitner	Black Club
915	Judi Radin-Kathie Wei	Marmic
916	Terence Reese-Jeremy Flint	Relay
917	John Collings-Paul Hackett	TRS
918	Eric Murray-Sami Kehela	Precision
919	Marty Bergen-Larry Cohen	Black Club
920	Hans Gothe-Anders Morath	Little Major
921	Karl Schneider-Hans Jellinek	Canary Club
922	Bob Hamman-Billy Eisenberg	Vienna Club
923	Paul Soloway-Bobby Goldman	Aces Scientific
924	John Armstrong-Tony Forrester	Walpurgis Diamond
925	Mike Lawrence-Bobby Goldman	Stone Age Acol + Paki Preempts

911   Munir-Fazli announced their methods as "Stone Age Acol with Paki Preempts."

912   Ghestem-Bacherich played Relay in the 50s and 60s.

913   Franco-Giovine (Italy) used Marmic, which featured a strong pass, in the early 50's. (The name comes from MARio-MIChele).

914   Lowenthal-Heitner developed the relay system known as the Canary Club.

915   Radin-Wei play Precision, of course.

916   Reese-Flint played the Little Major.

917   Collings-Hackett wielded the dreaded Walpurgis Diamond for Great Britain in the 1981 Bermuda Bowl.

918   Murray-Kehela call their style "Colonial Acol."

919   Bergen-Cohen play Two-Over-One with lots of extras.

920   Gothe-Morath (Sweden) play the Carrot Club. (Morath is known as "The Carrot" because of his red hair.)

921   Schneider-Jellinek used the Vienna Club to win the 1937 World Championship for Austria.

922   Hamman-Eisenberg used the Black Club in the 1971 Bermuda Bowl.

923   Soloway-Goldman play a strong club with super-light openings when nonvulnerable only.

924   Armstrong-Forrester played TRS (a medium pass system) for Great Britain in the 1987 Bermuda Bowl.

925   Lawrence-Goldman played Aces Scientific.

Would You Have Done Better?

Before 1989, when the U.S. lost to Brazil in the final, U.S. teams had won seven Bermuda Bowls in a row plus the 1988 World Open Team Olympiad. But there have been dark times when American world championship fortunes languished at rock bottom. U.S. players faced the problems in this quiz in world championship competition during the late 60s and early 70s — the middle of a frustrating dry spell. The 1969 Bermuda Bowl furnished many of the problems. That year, the last U.S. team selected through the pair-trials method went to Rio de Janeiro, turned in an abyssmal performance and failed to qualify for the final. Here's a chance to prove that if you had played, America wouldn't have had to wait until 1976 to recapture the Bermuda Bowl or 1988 to win the Vanderbilt Trophy. Your hand is presented above the seat you occupy. Good luck!

			K63
			9742
			KQJ532
VUL: NONE			—

WEST	NORTH	EAST	SOUTH
—	3♣	Pass	Pass
Dbl	Pass	Pass	?

What is your call? _____ 926

			KQJ1076
			85
			5
VUL: NONE			K432

WEST	NORTH	EAST	SOUTH
1♣	1♡	2◇	2♠
3◇	4◇	Pass	4♠
Pass	5♣	Pass	5◇
Pass	5♠	Pass	?

Do you agree with your 5◇ bid? What do you call now? _____ 927

J96
A10542
--
KQ1042   VUL: ALL

WEST	NORTH	EAST	SOUTH
1♡	Pass	2◇ ¹	2♠
Pass	Pass	2NT	Pass
3♣	Pass	3◇	Pass
?			

¹ Forcing to game

Do you like your pass over 2♠? What do you
call now? _____ 928

A7
AK9765
K5
1087   VUL: N-S

WEST	NORTH	EAST	SOUTH
--	1♡	3♣	4♡
5♣	?		

What do you call? _____ 929

K652
J32
10
VUL: ALL   AQ852

WEST	NORTH	EAST	SOUTH
1◇	Pass	2♣	Pass
3◇	Pass	?	

What do you call? _____ 930

KJ
2
KQ985
A10754

VUL: ALL

WEST	NORTH	EAST	SOUTH
--	--	1◇	4♡
Pass	Pass	?	

What do you call? _____ 931

KQ52
J932
Q1083
4   VUL: NONE

WEST	NORTH	EAST	SOUTH
--	--	1♡	1♠
?			

What do you call? _____ 932

Q762
10953
A10
A102   VUL: E-W

WEST	NORTH	EAST	SOUTH
--	--	Pass	1◇
1♠	?		

Not playing negative doubles, what do you call?
_____ 933

AK105
Q83
K65
J96

VUL: ALL

WEST	NORTH	EAST	SOUTH
--	Pass	1♠	Pass
Pass	Dbl	Pass	?

What do you call? _____ 934

Q62
107
K6532
Q74

VUL: ALL

WEST	NORTH	EAST	SOUTH
--	Pass	Pass	3♣
Dbl	4♣	4♡	Dbl
Pass	?		

What do you call? _____ 935

973
AQ62
KQ1085
6

VUL: ALL

WEST	NORTH	EAST	SOUTH
--	Pass	Pass	1♡
Dbl	2♡	?	

What do you call? _____ 936

VUL: E-W

$\qquad$ A98
$\qquad$ Q97
$\qquad$ 972
$\qquad$ 10764

WEST	NORTH	EAST	SOUTH
--	--	--	Pass
1♡	1♠	?	

What do you call? _____ 937

$\qquad$ K85
$\qquad$ 75
$\qquad$ KJ762
$\qquad$ J82

$\qquad$ A1032
$\qquad$ KQ
$\qquad$ 95
$\qquad$ AKQ76

WEST	NORTH	EAST	(You) SOUTH
--	Pass	Pass	1♣
Pass	1◊	Pass	1♠
Pass	2♣	Pass	3NT
All Pass			

Opening lead: ♡4

East wins the ace and returns the ♡10, West following with the 3. You take five rounds of clubs. West discards the ◊3 and ◊Q, East throws the ◊4, 8 and 10. On a spade lead to the king, West plays the queen. How do you continue? _____ 938

KQJ4
A4
A
VUL: NONE   KJ8763

WEST	NORTH	EAST	SOUTH
--	--	1♣	1♠
Pass	2♡	?	

What do you call? _____ 939

A53
J
A5
VUL: ALL   K1095432

WEST	NORTH	EAST	SOUTH
--	--	--	1♣
4♡	5♠	Pass	6♠
Pass	Pass	7♡	?

What do you call? _____ 940

7
532
Q8432
10732   VUL: E-W

WEST	NORTH	EAST	SOUTH
Pass	Pass	2♠	Dbl
4♠	Pass	Pass	Dbl
Pass	?		

What do you call? _____ 941

Q104
AQJ10642
AQ
Q   VUL: NONE

WEST	NORTH	EAST	SOUTH
—	1♥	Pass	2♦
?			

What do you call? _____ 942

                                                     A985
                                                     5
                                                     654
VUL: NONE   AK1095

WEST	NORTH	EAST	SOUTH
Pass	Pass	1♡	Dbl
Pass	1♠	Pass	Pass
2♡	2♠	3♡	?

What do you call? _____ 943

Q83
KJ4
954
Q954   VUL: N-S

WEST	NORTH	EAST	SOUTH
—	—	Pass	1♠
Dbl	2♠	Pass	3♦
Pass	?		

What do you call? _____ 944

AJ983
K952
1063
4

65
J74
KQ95
Q1098

(You)

WEST	NORTH	EAST	SOUTH
Pass	Pass	1♣	1♠
2♣	3♠	All Pass	

You lead the ♣10. South wins the ace, ruffs a club, leads a trump to his hand and ruffs another club. He next goes to the ♠A, East following, and leads the ◇10. East covers with the jack, and declarer follows with the 2. How do you defend? _____ 945

Q9532
--
Q642
9873

VUL: NONE

WEST	NORTH	EAST	SOUTH
--	1◇	1♡	?

What do you call? _____ 946

J103
A10
A54
VUL: N-S   AK976

WEST	NORTH	EAST	SOUTH
--	--	--	1♠
Pass	2♠	3♣	3♠
4♣	Pass	?	

What do you call? _____ 947

9752
J
1098
VUL: E-W   AQ1075

WEST	NORTH	EAST	SOUTH
--	--	Pass	1♡
1♠	2♡	?	

What do you call? _____ 948

AQJ4
A2
K5
VUL: ALL   KQJ82

WEST	NORTH	EAST	SOUTH
--	--	--	1NT (12-14)
Pass	Pass	Dbl	Pass
2♡	Pass	2NT	Pass
3♢	Pass	?	

What do you call? _____ 949

8643
10
AK63
AQ98

VUL: E-W

WEST	NORTH	EAST	SOUTH
—	—	Pass	1♠
Pass	4NT	Pass	5♡
Pass	5♠	Pass	Pass
?			

What do you call? _____ 950

87
AQJ72
10872
72

AQJ953
105
4
AK104

WEST	NORTH	EAST	SOUTH
—	—	Pass	1♠
Pass	1NT	2♢	2♠
3♢	3♠	Pass	4♠
Dbl	All Pass		

West leads the ♢A and shifts to the ♡6. What is your line of play?

_____

_____

951

A10
K86
A87
KQ1073

KQ9832
A9
QJ53
A

You land in 7♠ with no opposing bidding. West leads the ♡2. What is your line of play?

_____

_____

952

AQ74
Q7
QJ1054
AQ   VUL: N-S

WEST	NORTH	EAST	SOUTH
1♠	1NT	2♠	3◊
3♠	?		

What do you call? _____ 953

You hold: J98
            K7
            AKQ10
            KQ76

The opponents are vulnerable. After two passes, your right-hand opponent opens 1♠. What do you call? _____ 954

You hold: AK9653
            Q874
            AQ10
VUL: N-S   --

WEST	EAST
--	1♠
2♣	2♡
5♡	?

What do you call? _____ 955

            Q104
            Q10872
            KQ2
VUL: E-W   98

WEST	NORTH	EAST	SOUTH
--	Pass	Pass	1♡ (at most 16 pts)
Dbl	Pass	1NT	3♣
3◊	Pass	?	

What do you call? _____ 956

            AKJ72
            7
            1063
            K1097   VUL: NONE

WEST	NORTH	EAST	SOUTH
--	1♠	Pass	2♣
4♡	Pass	Pass	Dbl
Pass	?		

What do you call? _____ 957

—
A982
KQ9872
653   VUL: N-S

NORTH	SOUTH
—	2♣
2♠ 1	3♠
4♢	4♡
5♡	5NT
?	

1 Artificial, showing an ace and a king

What do you call? _____ 958

                                         1082
                                         A1086542
                                         AJ
VUL: ALL   2

WEST	NORTH	EAST	SOUTH
1♣	Pass	1♡	1♠
2♣	2♠	?	

What do you call? _____ 959

AJ873
J
KQ2
Q873   VUL: E-W

WEST	NORTH	EAST	SOUTH
1♠	Pass	2♣	Pass
3♣	Pass	3NT	Pass
?			

What do you call? _____ 960

```
                  10842
                  87
                  10832
                  Q103
K
J32
K9654
AJ42

WEST          NORTH        EAST        SOUTH
1◊            Pass         1♡          1♠
2♡            2♠           3♣ *        4♠
Pass          Pass         Dbl         All Pass
```

* longer clubs than hearts

You lead the ♡2. East wins the king and shifts to the ◊J. Declarer takes the ace and cashes the ♠A, East playing the 5. Next declarer leads the ◊7. How do you defend? _____ 961

                                        K3
                                        Q8
                                        A632
VUL: N-S   A7643

```
WEST          NORTH        EAST        SOUTH
--            2♠           Dbl         Redbl
Pass          Pass         2NT         Dbl
Pass          Pass         Redbl       Pass
3♡            Dbl          Pass        ?
```

What do you call? _____ 962

—
AQJ975
A92
AJ72

VUL: ALL

WEST	NORTH	EAST	SOUTH
—	Pass	Pass	1♡
Dbl	1♠	Dbl	2♡
4♠	Pass	Pass	?

What do you call? _____ 963

5432
KQJ82
QJ
98

VUL: NONE

WEST	NORTH	EAST	SOUTH
—	1♣	Pass	1♡
1♠	Pass	Pass	?

What do you call? _____ 964

J32
KJ108
108754
Q

VUL: ALL

WEST	NORTH	EAST	SOUTH
—	—	—	1◊
Pass	2◊	Pass	Pass
Dbl	Pass	2♡	3◊
Pass	Pass	3♡	Pass
Pass	?		

What do you call? _____ 965

926   The U.S. South passed. East had *six* clubs to the A-9, and a remorseless defense beat 3♣ doubled 900. 3◊ would have been much better.

927   After North made his second slam try with 5♣, we would have bid 6♠. At least the U.S. South was consistent — he bid 5◊, then passed 5♠. Since North held 98xx, AK10xxx, Axx, --, 6♠ was cold, and Thailand bid it in the other room.

928   In this uncomfortable position, the U.S. West rebid 4♣. East, out of options, took a 4♡ preference on Q10x, xx, AKJxxx, Ax, and all passed. The contract was hopeless, and a bad trump break added to the misery — down three. There were nine easy tricks in 3NT, and 2♠ doubled by South would have gone for 800.

929   The U.S. North placed partner with a singleton club and bid 5♡. Alas, South had a *doubleton* club and West had Q-10-x of hearts, so 5♡ went down. Of course, if North had passed 5♣ around, South would have doubled for a big plus.

930   The U.S. East tried 3♠, and West took a 4♣ preference. East went to 5♣ and went down a trick when dummy tabled x, Qx, AKQJxxx, KJx. On a similar auction at the other table, East for Italy bid 3NT over 3◊ and made it. We think 3♠ is the correct call, even though on this occasion it was unsuccessful.

931   The U.S. East tried 5♣ and was doubled. Dummy was as good as declarer could have hoped for — Qxx, Jxx, Ax, Qxxxx — but 5♣ still went down one. At the other table, East passed 4♡ — down two.

932   The U.S. West bid 3♡, limit raise. This backfired when the next hand jumped to 4♠, and East, holding 9, AK8764, 94, AJ82, bid 5♡. 5♡ was doubled for down two, while 4♠ would have gone down. Perhaps East should have passed 4♠ around, but we think West seduced him with his 3♡ jump. With more than half his points in spades, West should have bid a cautious 2♡.

933   The U.S. North hammered 1♠ for penalty, a questionable action with poor spade spots. South sat for the double despite a minimum hand and a singleton spade, and West, who had a seven-card spade suit, made an overtrick.

934   It was another bad time to try punishing a one-level contract. The U.S. South passed, and 1♠ doubled was unbeatable. If South had bid 1NT, his side would have gone plus.

935   South's double suggested far more defense than normal — his hand was AJx, x, Jxx, AJxxxx. 4♡ doubled would have been down one, but North ran to 5♣, a questionable action since a large minus seemed certain at that contract. In fact, 5♣ went down three, but the U.S. gained when the opponents forgot to double!

936   The U.S. East tried 2NT, a serious underbid when vulnerable at IMPs. West, with J10xxx, x, Axx, AK10x, could do no more, and the U.S. missed a game that was bid and made in the other room.

937   The U.S. East passed — probably, his four-card-major style was a factor. After two passes, West reopened with a double, and East took out to 2♡. West then passed with QJx, AKJ10x, J10x, AK, missing the good notrump game.

938   The U.S. South finessed with the ♠10, following the principle of restricted choice, and went down when West won with the bare jack. In the replay, a French declarer guessed to drop the ♠J, possibly because East had never discarded an "idle fifth" spade.

939   The U.S. East risked 3♣ on his broken suit and was promptly doubled for -300. In the replay East passed over 2♡ and conceded only 140.

940   The U.S. South eyed his losing heart and doubled. The deal was a freak, and 7♡ doubled could be set only one. Since South had failed to cuebid 6♡ over 5♠, it would have been safe to pass 7♡ around. North, with KQJxxx, —, Qxxx, AQJ, might have pressed on to 7♠.

In the other room North jumped to 6♠ at his first turn, and West (with 0-9-4-0 distribution) saved at 7♡. North passed, and South bid 7♠, making, handing the U.S. a 19-IMP loss.

941   The U.S. North ran to 4NT, and N-S wound up going down in 6♡. 4♠ would have been down two.

942 The U.S. West jumped to 4♡, a strange action with such good defense. He was doubled and beaten three tricks. A 2♡ or 3♡ overcall would have avoided disaster.

943 The U.S. South bid 3♠ and was doubled. North was lucky to escape for down one. In the other room 3♡ went down. North, not too surprisingly, held four good hearts. Perhaps he should have been allowed to make the final decision.

944 The U.S. North bid 3NT. South, 5-5 in spades and diamonds, converted to 4♠, down three. The lesson: When partner makes a new-suit game try, pay scant attention to general strength; look at your holdings in partner's suits.

945 The full deal was:

```
                    AJ983
                    K952
                    1063
                    4
        65                      72
        J74                     A108
        KQ95                    AJ8
        Q1098                   KJ732
                    KQ104
                    Q63
                    742
                    A65
```

The U.S. West let East's ◊J hold. East cashed the ◊A and led another diamond to the queen. Forced to break hearts, West led the jack. Declarer guessed right, putting up dummy's king, and made his contract.

Since East had the ♡8, West could have beaten 3♠ by leading a low heart instead of the jack. But the best defense is to overtake the ◊J with the queen and lead the ♡J. Now if declarer puts up the ♡K, East wins the ace, cashes the ◊A and leads to the ◊K so West can lead another heart. Even if declarer holds the ♡8, he still must guess right on the lead of the jack.

946   The U.S. South bid 1♠. N-S were never in the auction again, and E-W bid to 4♡ and made it. At the other table South chose a raise to 2◊, enabling North to take a good 5◊ save over 4♡.

947   The U.S. East visualized a singleton spade in West's hand and bid 5♣. West did have a singleton spade, but that was why he had bid 4♣. He had little else (x, K9xx, xxx, Jxxxx), and 5♣ went down. At the other table, E-W bid and made a club partial.

948   The U.S. East jumped to 4♠, and South competed to 5♡. West, with a good spade-diamond two-suiter, went to 5♠, down one. 5♡ would have gone down two.

It seems that West might have made a better decision if East had bid clubs before raising spades, suggesting the location of his side strength.

949   The U.S. East persisted with 3NT and was doubled for 1100. A disciplined 3♡ preference would have saved the day.

950   The U.S. West thought for a long time and passed. The winning action was to balance with 5NT, since this was the full deal:

```
                          KQ72
                          KJ85432
                          7
                          2
        8643                              --
        10                               Q6
        AK63                             J109542
        AQ98                             K10765
                          AJ1095
                          A97
                          Q8
                          J43
```

5♠ made. At the other table an Italian E-W pair got into the auction, and the U.S. N-S had to push to 6♠ over 6♣. West cashed the minor-suit aces for down one.

951

	87	
	AQJ72	
	10872	
	72	
K1042		6
63		K984
A53		KQJ96
Q653		J98
	AQJ953	
	105	
	4	
	AK104	

The U.S. declarer took the heart finesse, losing, and a trump return doomed the contract. Had declarer risen with the ♡A, he could have crossruffed diamonds and clubs, eventually catching West in a trump endplay and making the doubled game.

952   The U.S. declarer (and the Italian declarer at the other table) took the ♡A and cashed the A-K of spades. West showed out. Not enough entries remained for a trump coup against East, so the grand slam went down.

The correct line: ♡A, ♣A, ♠K, ♠A, club ruff, ◇Q led. West, who has the ◇K, covers, and the ace wins. ♣K, ♣Q, ♣10 pitching diamonds. East must discard on the clubs. Then diamond ruff and a heart to the king, arriving at the coup position.

953   The U.S. North bid 3NT, which was passed out. East led a heart from K-J-x-x-x, and the defense cashed five heart tricks. In the replay, North for Italy jumped to 5◇, which made.

954   The U.S. player who held these cards tried 2◇, passed out and down one. His counterpart preferred a 1NT overcall despite the lack of a spade stopper. 1NT made when dummy furnished help in spades.

955   The U.S. East correctly interpreted West's rebid as asking for a diamond control, but ambiguity crept into the auction when East continued with 5NT, intending it as the Grand Slam Force. West, whose hand was —, AKJ9, xxxx, AKQxx, thought East was showing the ◊K — he signed off in 6♡.

         Clearly (to us, anyway) East should have bid at least 6◊ over 5♡. In fact, a jump to 7♡ is not out of the question. After all, how could West bid 5♡ with no diamond control if he also lacked one of the top trump honors?

956   This was a hard-luck deal for the U.S. Our East tried 3NT. West held AKxx, —, Axxxxx, A10x, and everything looked wonderful until diamonds split 4-0. In the replay, East for Italy raised diamonds, and the Italian pair reached 5◊, losing only a diamond and a club.

957   The U.S. North made (what looks like) the normal pull to 5♣, which went down. The South hand was xx, Kxx, K9xx, Axxx. Perfect defense would have beaten 4♡ three tricks. (For the West hand, see problem 942.) The swing really occurred because the U.S. South chose a 2♣ response, whereas the Brazilian South at the other table responded 2◊! Anyone for 1NT? By limiting his hand on the first round of the auction, South would have helped the partnership handle any further bidding.

958   The U.S. North thought his trumps were as good as they could be in the circumstances — wouldn't he have bid 6♡ over 4♡ with A-Q-x-x? He therefore jumped to 7♡. South passed with AKQxx, KJxx, A10, AK and lost a trick to the trump queen. Down one.

         Perhaps North should stress his long, strong suit by bidding 6◊ or 7◊ over 5NT. N-S could then stop in 7◊ or 7NT.

959   The U.S. East overstated his hand by jumping to 4♡. West, who held Ax, K, xxxx, AKJ9xx, cuebid 4♠, heard 5◊(!) in reply and jumped to 6♡. Desperation play led to down four.

960   3NT was the best spot and would have made, but the U.S. West removed to 4♣. East then got overly excited with the following hand: 10x, Kxx, A10xx, AK9x, and bid himself into a hopeless 6♣.

961

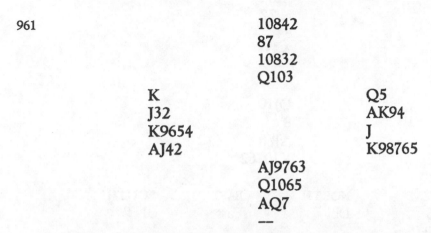

```
                         10842
                         87
                         10832
                         Q103
        K                                Q5
        J32                              AK94
        K9654                            J
        AJ42                             K98765
                         AJ9763
                         Q1065
                         AQ7
                         —
```

The U.S. sustained a painful loss when West had a brainstorm and *ducked* the second diamond. East ruffed dummy's 10, cashed the ♡A and led a club. Declarer ruffed and threw dummy's remaining diamonds on the ♡Q and ♡10, making 4♠ doubled.

962   The U.S. South pulled to 3♠. North went on to 4♠, which might have been made but wasn't. North had a reasonable defensive hand with ♡A107, and 3♡ doubled would have been down a couple.

963   The U.S. South doubled, but North's 1♠ bid had been a bluff — E-W were cold for 5♠. South's winning action was to bid as high as 6♡. He probably would have taken 11 tricks at hearts.

964   A pass would have been a excellent decision — North, not unexpectedly, had a minimum hand with a good spade holding, and 1♠ would have been beaten. However, the U.S. South tried 2♡ and went down.

965   The U.S. North passed, and 3♡ went down four tricks. Such chances seldom came along against the Italians, so perhaps North should have considered doubling.

The Last Roundup

A872
KJ72
84
A53

QJ10
8
AJ76
K10762

WEST	NORTH	EAST	SOUTH
1◇	Dbl	Pass	3NT
All Pass			

IMPs, both vulnerable. West leads the ♡3. Plan the play. _____

966

AQ
A106
QJ1082
AQ3

KJ953
54
K6
J542

WEST	NORTH	EAST	SOUTH
--	1◇	1♠	Pass
Pass	Dbl	Pass	1NT
Pass	2NT	Pass	3NT
All Pass			

Matchpoints, N-S vulnerable. West leads the ♠8. Plan the defense. _____ 967

IMPs, none vulnerable. You hold: KJ108653
                                      8
                                      J3
                                      Q106

WEST	NORTH	EAST	SOUTH
1◊	Pass	1NT	?

Would you preempt? _____ 968

```
                    Q10
                    J652
                    K654
                    J97
      J8642                      9
      K987                       A104
      92                         AQJ10
      K2                         Q10864
                    AK753
                    Q3
                    873
                    A53
```

WEST	NORTH	EAST	SOUTH
Pass	Pass	1◊	1♠
All Pass			

Matchpoints, both vulnerable. West led the ◊9.
East won the 10 and switched to the ♣6, ducked
to the king. South won the club continuation with
the ace and put East in with a club. West threw
the ♡9. East led a heart to the queen and king,
and West switched back to diamonds. East took the
◊J and ◊A, then led the ◊Q, on which South
discarded his concealed ♡3. West ruffed and
returned a heart — 5, 10, ruff. South then led a
spade to the 10, cashed the ♠Q and took the last
two tricks with the ♠AK, escaping for down one.
What error did East commit? _____ 969

TIME LIMIT: 10 SECONDS. In a Spingold semifinal several years ago, Lou Bluhm-Tom Sanders registered the unusual score of +340. What happened? _____ 970

> AQ109
> 962
> 1063
> 743
>
> 63
> A53
> AKJ9
> A852

IMPs, both vulnerable. South opened 1NT, and all passed. West led the ♡7 — 2, king, 3. East returned the J♡. Declarer ducked again, and West overtook with the queen and forced out the ♡A, East discarding a low spade.

South tried a spade to the 9, losing to East's jack. Declarer took the ♣Q return with the ace and cashed the ◊AK, hoping the queen would fall. When it did not, South led a spade to the queen. This lost to the king, and the defense cashed out for down three.

Since East held the ◊Q, South could have made his contract. Was his play unreasonable? _____ 971

Construct an auction to the best contract. West is dealer.

WEST	EAST
AQ742	K5
AJ4	KQ106
KJ103	Q72
J	8632

————	————
972	973

————	————
974	975

————	————
976	977

Pass

A2
9752
K10852
83

WEST	NORTH	EAST	SOUTH
—	1♡	Pass	1♠
Pass	2♣	Pass	2♠
Pass	3♠	Pass	4♠
All Pass			

Matchpoints, all vulnerable. What should West lead? ———— 978

IMPS   AKJ
VUL: ALL   64
             A75
             Q9752

753   96
J73   A9852
K863   J109
A64   K83

            Q10842
            KQ10
            Q42
            J10

WEST	NORTH	EAST	SOUTH
—	1♣	Pass	1♠
Pass	2♠	Pass	2NT
Pass	3NT	All Pass	

West led the ◊3 to the 5, 9 and queen. South reached dummy with the ♠K and led the ♣2 — 3, jack, ace. After some thought, West switched to the ♡3. East won the ace and returned a heart. Declarer won, knocked out the ♣K and ended up with an overtrick when he could have been beaten. Whose fault on defense? ____ 979

North, your partner, opens 1◊. East overcalls 1♠, and you bid 1NT. North raises to 2NT. Which of the following hands is the best for a bid of 3NT? ____ 980 Which is the worst? ____ 981

       (a)   K94, 7652, A85, Q84

       (b)   A85, 7652, Q84, K94

       (c)   Q84, 7652, K94, A85

       (d)   K94, 7652, Q84, A85

       (e)   A85, 7652, K94, Q84

       (f)   Q84, 7652, A85, K94

10642
J10
AJ106
K53

AKQ853
A3
Q94
76

WEST	NORTH	EAST	SOUTH
--	--	--	1♠
Pass	2♠	Pass	3♠
Pass	4♠	All Pass	

IMPs. West leads the ♡ 6. Plan the play.
_____ 982

86
85
AJ10753
Q107

QJ1073   K952
J942   Q10763
K4   86
83   KJ

A4
AK
Q92
A96542

South was declarer at 3NT. How did he go down?
_____ 983

What was Charles Goren's profession before he
became a full-time bridge guru? _____ 984

	YOU	PARTNER
	1♡	1NT
	2♣	3◇

Which of the following hands is partner most likely to hold? _____ 985

86	A8	875	76	K106
Q7	87	6	84	76
KQJ965	AJ107652	AK3	AK63	KQ953
764	76	J108652	J10865	Q43
(a)	(b)	(c)	(d)	(e)

A1098   What's the best play for three tricks? _____

□   _____ 986

Kxxx

                5
                AKJ53
                965
                AK76
                          AJ9
                          92
                          A1043
                          J985

WEST	NORTH	EAST	SOUTH
—	1♡	Pass	1♠
Pass	2♣	Pass	3♠
Pass	4♠	All Pass	

IMPs, both vulnerable. West leads the ◇2. Plan the defense. _____ 987

WEST	EAST	
A762	KQJ3	
842	AQ3	
AK76	Q432	
A10	Q3	

WEST	EAST	
1NT ¹	2◇ ²	¹ 15-17
2♠	3♠ ³	2 Forcing Stayman
4♣	4♡	3 Forcing, invites cuebidding
4♠	5♠	
6♠	Pass	

This terrible slam went down two. Whose fault? _____ 988

TIME LIMIT: 10 SECONDS. It's possible to score 50 points at duplicate, but not 60. What's the next higher unattainable score divisible by 10? _____

989

WEST	EAST
QJ92	10653
AQ3	K4
8	AKJ53
AKJ62	83

WEST	EAST	
1♣	1◇	
1♠	3♠ ¹	¹ Invitational
4♣	4◇	
4♡	5♡	
6♠	Pass	

6♠ was not a winning contract. Who do you blame? _____ 990

When your partner tables the dummy, you see he has grossly underbid, causing you to miss a cold game. What is your best action? _____ 991

(a) Inform the opponents you're in the wrong spot.

(b) Castigate partner's bidding immediately.

(c) Play the hand, then castigate partner's bidding.

(d) Say nothing but play hurriedly, getting the disaster behind you quickly.

(e) Say nothing but try to take as many tricks as possible — you might save an IMP.

```
                         K5
                         A65
                         K10
                         AQ10865
          1087                        QJ
          K872                        J109
          832                         AQJ9654
          943                         7
                         A96432
                         Q43
                         7
                         KJ2
```

WEST	NORTH	EAST	SOUTH
—	1NT	2◇	3♠
Pass	3NT	Pass	4♠
All Pass			

Matchpoints, neither vulnerable. West led the ◇2 — 10, J, 7. East switched to the ♡J — 3, 8, ace. South then cashed the ♠K and ♠A and led a third spade. West won (East discarding the ◇6) and tried to put partner in with the ◇A to lead another heart through. Declarer ruffed and took the rest with the clubs — making five. Whose fault on defense for not holding the hand to four?

_____ 992

IMPs, both vulnerable. As South, you hold:

8
A863
Q10764
A76

West, the dealer, opens 1♡. North and East pass.
Do you balance? _____ 993

Suppose you choose to bid 2◊; North raises to 4◊.
Do you go on? _____ 994

Which of the following ideas are valid? _____ 995

(a) The Law of Total Tricks
(b) The Law of Symmetry
(c) The Law of Balanced Distribution
(d) The queen always lies over the jack
(e) The principle of restricted choice

(You may choose more than one.)

```
Q9753
A98
KJ102
K
                        106
                        J4
                        83
                        AQJ10943
```

WEST	NORTH	EAST	SOUTH
—	—	3♣	Pass
Pass	Dbl	Pass	3♡
All Pass			

IMPs, neither vulnerable. West leads the ♠K and shifts to the ♣5. You win and return a spade to West's ace. West switches back to the ♣6, ruffed in dummy. South then leads the ♠Q. Do you . . .
(a) ruff with the 4?
(b) ruff with the jack?
(c) discard?   _____ 996

MATCHPOINTS
```
            QJ
            AJ93
            A753
            K64


            K106
            Q10652
            92
            A75
```

WEST	NORTH	EAST	SOUTH
—	1◇	Pass	1♡
Pass	2♡	Pass	3♡
Pass	4♡	All Pass	

West leads the ♣J. Plan the play. _____ 997

K6
Q97652
AQ83
6

A
AK
KJ975
A8532

With no opposition bidding, you arrive at a grand slam in diamonds. The opening lead is the ♠Q. Plan the play.

_____ 998

AQ
J73
107542
QJ9

K642
AK5
KQ6
AK4

The contract is 6NT. The opening lead is the ♣8. Plan the play.

_____ 999

                        K65
                        853
                        AKQ1094
                        7

                        AQ4
                        K74
                        52
                        Q10642

WEST	NORTH	EAST	SOUTH
---	1◊	Dbl	Redbl
Pass	Pass	2♣	Dbl
2♡	Pass	Pass	2NT
Pass	3NT	All Pass	

IMPs, neither side vulnerable. West leads the ♡6. East wins the ace and returns the ♡2. Plan the play.

_____

_____ 1,000

            A105
            A732
            J105
            K94
                        J4
                        KQ1064
                        A63
                        1072

WEST	NORTH	EAST	SOUTH
---	---	---	1◊
Pass	1♡	Pass	1NT
Pass	2NT	Pass	3NT
Pass	Pass	Dbl	All Pass

Opening lead: ♡8. Plan the defense.

_____ 1,001

966

	A872	
	KJ72	
	84	
	A53	
K6		9543
A1053		Q964
Q1095		K32
QJ4		98
	QJ10	
	8	
	AJ76	
	K10762	

In the 1969 Bermuda Bowl, Eddie Kantar correctly played the ♡K from dummy. He then set up the clubs, took the winning spade finesse and rounded out the contract with the ◊A.

If declarer plays any other heart at trick one, East can win and beat the game with a diamond switch.

967   If declarer plays the ♠Q from dummy, East must let it hold. South surely has ♠10xxx — hence, a double stopper — and 3NT is probably cold if he has the ◊A plus the ♡K or ♣K. Assuming West holds the ◊A, East must force declarer to win one of his two spade tricks early. Then West will have a spade to lead when he wins the ◊A. The full deal:

	AQ	
	A106	
	QJ1082	
	AQ3	
82		KJ953
Q9872		54
A54		K6
1087		J542
	10764	
	KJ3	
	973	
	K96	

968   We could accept a 2♠ bid — you might even buy it there, or maybe partner can raise — but a jump to 3♠ is poor. First, the opponents have exchanged enough information that preemption has less to gain. Second, why panic? You hold the ranking suit and will enjoy an edge in a competitive auction. But if West has a strong hand, you'll do better to pass.

969   Sure, East can cash the ♡A before leading the fourth diamond, but what if South is 6-1-3-3? East's error came at trick nine when he played the ♡10! At that point, he knows that declarer has only trumps left. To follow with the ♡A, hiding the distribution, costs nothing. If East had done this, South surely would have counted East for 2-2-4-5 distribution and played to pull trumps with the queen, then ace-king.

970   Bluhm played 1♢ doubled, making three, not vulnerable. (Take credit if you said 1♣.)

971
```
                          AQ109
                          962
                          1063
                          743
        852                              KJ74
        Q10874                           KJ
        84                               Q752
        K106                             QJ9
                          63
                          A53
                          AKJ9
                          A852
```

Since South needed three spade tricks to make his contract, he was playing West for K-x-x. But East would never have thrown a spade early from J-x-x-x, so declarer's play was wrong. He should have finessed in diamonds.

972–977   We suggest:

WEST	EAST
1♠	1NT
2♢	2NT
3♡	4♡
Pass	

978　The winning lead is the ♠2. The full deal:

```
                        KJ
                        AKJ83
                        7
                        K10654
        A2                              854
        9752                            106
        K10852                          AQ93
        83                              QJ97
                        Q109763
                        Q4
                        J64
                        A2
```

Since the bidding suggests that North has 2-5-2-4 or 2-5-1-5 pattern, West's main concern is stopping ruffs in dummy. But if West leads the ace and another trump, declarer will draw trumps and run the hearts and clubs. A low-trump lead lets West keep control.

979　West was unlucky — his heart switch could have been the killer. However, most of the blame goes to East. We can't charge him for not rising with the ♣K to clear the diamonds (although it would have been neat), but we can charge him for an earlier, subtle error. From the play to the first trick, West was afraid that declarer had ◇QJx; then a diamond continuation would cost a trick. But if East plays the ◇10 at trick one (instead of the 9), West will think that another diamond lead cannot cost. Perhaps he will continue diamonds as the best chance to beat the contract.

A similar but better known position is:

```
                        862

        A953                            QJ10

                        K74
```

When West leads the 3, East may induce partner to continue the suit by playing the *jack*.

980   (c) is best. You spend only two of your high-card points to take a trick in spades, and you have a fast winner in clubs and a king that is working hard.

981   Probably (e) is worst. Your spade stopper is primary — bad news — and the ♣Q is worth less than the ◇Q in (b).

982

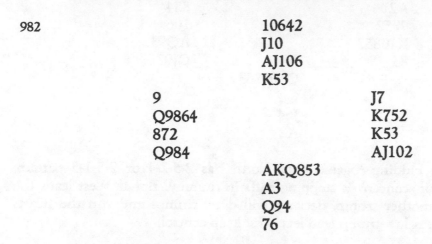

```
                          10642
                          J10
                          AJ106
                          K53
         9                              J7
         Q9864                          K752
         872                            K53
         Q984                           AJ102
                          AKQ853
                          A3
                          Q94
                          76
```

Declarer must duck the first trick, of course. Now West can never win a heart trick and lead a club through dummy's king.

As the cards lie, you go down if you win the first trick. You didn't miss this one, did you?

983   Declarer took the opening spade lead and planned a diamond finesse. To give himself an extra chance, however, he first cashed the ♣A. East dropped the king(!), and South, mentally patting himself on the back, led a club to the 10.

984   Goren was an attorney.

985   (c) is correct. According to most experts, partner's sequence promises a big club fit with diamond values. (a) would bid 2◇ over 2♣. (b) would respond 2◇ to 1♡, planning to rebid 3◇. (d) would raise 2♣ to 3♣. (e) would bid 2NT over 2♣.

986   It's best to lead the 10, 9 or 8, and run it if second hand plays low. After this loses to an honor, cash your king next. This line loses only to a singleton honor in one particular hand (i.e., West). Equally good is to do the same thing in the other direction: Lead toward dummy and finesse when West plays low. Then cash dummy's ace on the second round, losing only to East's singleton queen or jack.

This play (94%) is better than cashing an honor to begin with, which loses to any small singleton or void behind the honor. The current *Encyclopedia of Bridge* (4th edition) errs by saying that if you think one hand is more likely to be shorter than the other, you should finesse through the assumed length first. Instead, finesse through the assumed shortness first, and on the next round lay down the honor in front of the assumed length. (Thanks to the famous Jack Dreyfus, of New York, for bringing this combination to our attention.)

987   Win the ◇A and return a diamond to cash what tricks you can. Otherwise, your only chance to do something positive is in trumps. You may create a surprise trick by playing your *jack* on the first lead from dummy. If South reads you for the doubleton A-J, he will continue with a low trump.

5
AKJ53
965
AK76

762	AJ9
10876	92
KJ82	A1043
104	J985

KQ10843
Q4
Q7
Q32

Note that if you follow with the ♠9, declarer will take the percentage play of finessing the 10 and make his game.

988   Maybe West shouldn't have cuebid 4♣, but his minimum did contain good controls.

       We'd give East almost all the blame. With only one ace and one king, he should give up on slam when West signs off in 4♠. If trumps split 3-2, East's ♠J is wasted. And East's 5♠ was a poor bid because it was ambiguous — East intended it as a general slam try, but West understandably thought he was *forced* to bid slam with a diamond control.

989   **220.**

990   We blame East. Without an honor in trumps, his 5♡ cuebid was too aggressive. If the East hand had been K10xx, Kx, AJxxx, xx — which is what West expected — slam would have a reasonable play.

991   We hope you favored (e).

992   East is to blame. Granted, he put up a nice defense by switching to a heart rather than trying to cash his ◇A. However, once East guessed correctly that partner was not leading a singleton diamond, he should have dumped that ◇A on the third round of trumps. This could only mean one thing: Cash whatever you have in hearts, because that's all we're going to get.

993   We'd balance. The opponents could be better off in spades, but you do have two defensive tricks in case they suddenly decide to bid a game.

       Partscore swings at IMPs can add up fast. If you sell out and West makes 1♡ when you could have made a partscore, the cost will be a painful 5 IMPs.

994   When North raises to 4◇, we think you should bid 5◇. North must have a good hand and a singleton to aim at an 11-trick contract. If he had a stiff heart, he would have acted over 1♡. If he had a stiff spade, the opponents would have bid spades. So North has a stiff club, and your ♣A is just the right card. Partner may have heart length, but the danger of a defensive ruff is lessened when you hold the ♡A.

995   Only (a), (c) and (e) are accepted. Many good players swear by the Law of Total Tricks, which states that if each side plays a deal in its best trump suit, the total tricks available equal the total number of trumps.

The Law of Balanced Distribution says that the more symmetric of two specific holdings is more likely, and two equally symmetric holdings are equally likely. In other words, if Q-J-4-3-2 are missing, Q-4, 3-2, Q-4-3 and 4-3-2 are equally probable. Q, 2, Q-J-4-3 and Q-4-3-2 are less symmetric and therefore less probable.

The principle of restricted choice is a mathematically-based concept.

The Law of Symmetry suggests that a player with, say, 5-4-3-1 shape will find the remaining cards in his long suit distributed 4-3-1 around the table. This so-called law and "The queen lies over the jack" are completely unreliable.

996

	Q9753	
	A98	
	KJ102	
	K	
AKJ2		106
K105		J4
964		83
765		AQJ10943
	84	
	Q7632	
	AQ75	
	82	

In the 1965 Scientist-Traditionalist match, an expert East ruffed the ♠Q with the 4. This play was a clear error — South could not have a useful discard on the ♠Q — and it was duly punished when declarer overruffed with the 6 and led the ♡Q, pinning the jack to make a hopeless contract. Note that ruffing with the ♡J would have been equally fatal.

997

	QJ	
	AJ93	
	A753	
	K64	
A987		5432
84		K7
K1064		QJ8
J109		Q832
	K106	
	Q10652	
	92	
	A75	

A breather. Win the first trick in dummy and lead the ♠Q, setting up a discard for your club loser. If you carelessly take the first trick with the ♣A and finesse in trumps, you go down when East wins the king and returns a club. (As a matter of fact, if you win the first trick in your hand, you go down even if you start spades — West wins the second spade and locks you in dummy with a club.) If you missed this one, please get one of the easier books in this series.

998

	K6	
	Q97652	
	AQ83	
	6	
QJ1084		97532
J1084		3
2		1064
KJ9		Q1074
	A	
	AK	
	KJ975	
	A8532	

A famous deal. Win the ♠A, cash the ◇K and ♡A, go to dummy with the ◇Q and discard the ♡K on the ♠K. Then ruff a heart, lead a diamond to the ace and ruff another heart. Finally, ♣A, club ruff and claim (dummy is down to the good Q-9-7 of hearts).

999

<pre>
                          AQ
                          J73
                          107542
                          QJ9
          J73   10985
          Q964   1082
          93   AJ8
          8752   1063
                          K642
                          AK5
                          KQ6
                          AK4
</pre>

Win the first trick *in your hand*, keeping club entries flexible. Cross to dummy with the ♠A and lead a diamond to the king. Return to the ♠Q and lead another diamond. If East wins and returns a club, you can win in hand, unblock the ◊Q and get to dummy with the ♣Q to cash the diamonds. The slam can be beaten if you win the first trick in dummy.

1,000

<pre>
                          K65
                          853
                          AKQ1094
                          7
          932   J1087
          Q106   AJ92
          J8763   —
          53   AKJ98
                          AQ4
                          K74
                          52
                          Q10642
</pre>

West probably has only three hearts — East returned the 2 at the second trick, suggesting four, and West would have shown a four-card major over the redouble. Since East bypassed a major to bid clubs, he is sure to have at least five (West certainly would not run from 2♣ doubled with three clubs). If East also has four spades for his takeout double, there isn't room in his hand for a diamond. Win the ♡K and lead a diamond to the 10.

1,001

A105
A732
J105
K94

Q9762   J4
85   KQ1064
Q7   A63
J863   1072

K83
J9
K9842
AQ5

Let declarer win the first trick. If partner has an entry plus a second heart to lead, the contract will fail. On the actual deal, declarer will win the first trick, cross to the ♣K and lead the ◇J. Partner will get in with the queen and continue hearts. If you win the first trick with the ♡Q and bang down the ♡K, dummy's ♡7 will stand up and you will never win a trick with your fifth heart.

When this hand was played, the player sitting East found the winning defense. But when his partner won the ◇Q, he shifted to a spade, thinking East held nothing good in hearts (despite his penalty double). Which brings us to problem . . .

1,002   If you are East and do duck the first heart trick, then watch in horror as partner shifts to spades, your best action will be to:

(a) Immediately lunge across the table and grab him by the throat.
(b) Say "No hearts, partner?" and when he fails to answer, then lunge at him.
(c) Assume partner has no more hearts, and kick yourself for ducking the first trick.
(d) Purchase a gift-copy of *The Bridge Today 1,001 Workbook* and send it to partner for Christmas.

We won't tell you the answer; however, you probably know which one we like best. By the way, thanks for doing this book. We sincerely hope you've enjoyed it.

— *Frank Stewart, Pamela Granovetter, Matthew Granovetter.*